# DATE DUE

# The Fairleigh Dickinson University

## Conference on Oceanology, St. Croix, Virgin Islands, 1967.

EDITED BY

PETER SAMMARTINO, Ph.D.
*Chancellor, Fairleigh Dickinson University*

FAIRLEIGH DICKINSON UNIVERSITY PRESS
Rutherford, New Jersey
1968

# FOREWORD

The three-day Fairleigh Dickinson University Conference on Oceanology, held in June 1967 at St. Croix, U.S. Virgin Islands, featured four two-hour sessions of presentations by outstanding authorities, followed by discussions. All proceedings, including question periods, were recorded on tape, and the papers were submitted to the speakers for editing.

In attendance were representatives from 51 colleges and universities, and 27 professional and learned societies, government agencies, and industries. The theme of the conference was "Man returning to the sea for knowledge and abundance," and its purpose was to enable the University to seek guidance and assistance in launching the new marine biology laboratory.

The scope of the conference was to discuss in general terms the importance of the sea program from the point of view of the United States, and also in the light of international well-being and harmony. It was involved with aquaculture, marine biology, physical oceanography, chemical oceanography, ocean engineering and sea laws.

The final ceremony of the conference was the official ground breaking for the Marine Biology Laboratory which is made possible by the generous gift of Fairleigh S. Dickinson, Jr., of the University's Board of Trustees.

The completion of this book would have been impossible without the invaluable assistance of Olive O.

[iii]

# FOREWORD

Foster. She was not only present at the conference, but accomplished the almost impossible task of assembling the speeches, which were imperfectly recorded because of the breakdown of equipment in the warm weather, and preparing them for publication in the months following the conference.

May 15, 1968                                      Peter Sammartino

# CONTENTS

**[v]**

I

# DEVELOPMENT OF THE NATIONAL PROGRAM IN OCEAN SCIENCE AND TECHNOLOGY: A VIEW FROM THE EXECUTIVE BRANCH OF GOVERNMENT

Robert B. Abel, M.E.A.

*Head, Office of Sea Grant Programs, National Science Foundation*

Oceanography represents a curve of history which is quite exponential. If one wishes to go far enough back in the literature he can examine perhaps a hundred or a hundred and fifty years of charting and mapping, accompanied by pockets of some rather excellent research in marine biology, until about the time of World War II when, for several reasons, it was discovered that the sea did actually contain real wealth.

Ten or fifteen years of somewhat accelerated research followed, mostly anti-submarine warfare-motivated. A moderate amount of oceanographic surveying took place in the middle 1950's. Since then the curve has risen very rapidly, until one confronts a kaleidoscope of accelerated oceanographic research both basic and applied. Now the phrase ''ocean engineering'' is becoming more and more popularized, and advanced development in science and technology is coming into an era where it faces institutional problems. Thus the social sciences including law, economics, and administration, have now become involved. This development apparently is one of the earmarks of a maturing program.

[1]

# NATIONAL PROGRAM IN
# OCEAN SCIENCE

If one wants to identify the original catalyst, it is probably simplest to return to the last decade, when the National Academy of Sciences formed an energetic and imaginative Committee on Oceanography; this Committee, after a period of deliberation, issued a series of documents called "Oceanography 1960–1970." These documents, which combined imagination, common sense, and really incredible timing, became known to the public and the Congress at the precise moment when the whole country was becoming science-oriented, perhaps motivated by Sputnik. The results probably exceeded anything dreamed of by the perpetrators.

Many federal agencies discovered at this time that they had interests in the ocean. Most of them were very largely involved, and great interest was beginning to emerge, with the science of the seas as the common denominator. A governmental group was formed (somewhat parallel to the Academy group, which represented the science community) called the Interagency on Oceanography (ICO). It was effective, in that at least it did coordinate oceanographic programs for and through about twenty to twenty-five agencies.

This campaign proved sufficiently effective so that Congress, after six years of mulling the situation over, decided to enact some fairly strong legislation, and formed a National Council for Marine Research and Engineering Development. At the same time a commission was formed to see what was going on, what needed to be done, and how we should go about doing it. The Council itself was formed at the cabinet level with the Vice-President as Chairman. The Council's first job was to propose some kind of a national program for ocean development. The ICO was assigned, drawing on its own reservoir of experience and expertise, to determine the areas demanding attention and those ripe for exploitation. These included the areas of international cooperation (which will be described further by Dr. Maxwell); the increased attention to food from the sea (which Dr. Schaefer will talk about in some detail); the National Sea Grant Program, which I can promise you will hear more about in a few minutes; and a comprehensive study of data systems including the entire spectrum of data management from initial concept through processing systems to ultimate utilization. It included a study of estuaries, that is, the marine environment which extends man's terrestrial environment to the sea; an expanded survey for mineral wealth that Mr. Bascom will speak about; oceanographic prediction techniques; and finally, elaboration of the Navy's Deep Ocean Technology Program, generally built around the problem of search and recovery techniques in the deep undersea. These were sent up to the Council. The Council mulled them over and accepted suggestions from several other quarters.

The President then issued to Congress a report entitled "Marine Science—A Year of Transition," in which these programs were spelled out as areas requiring some priority attention on the part of the government. First of all, instrumentation had certainly been the bane of oceanographers; it was inevitable that immediately out of the sight of land everything would go out at once. There were no filling stations, and no drugstore around the corner, nor sources of spare parts. Instrumentation can now be considered to be far more reliable, capable of maintaining far more depth, and far more susceptible to automation.

Computer technology itself has been applied to all facets of oceanographic measurements and data processing. People now speak in terms of automatic recording stations—buoys—not perhaps replacing ships so much as augmenting them and enabling the gathering of data at decreased time intervals, with greater scope of areal coverage at the same time.

Oceanographers are thinking in terms of wedding space to ocean technology, and using satellite systems which will recover vast amounts of oceanographic data. Vehicles themselves have undergone radical change. Oceanographers before this decade were constrained to use hulls made over from anything, from warships to life rafts, but specially configured hulls for oceanography were introduced in 1960. The United States today certainly does possess the most advanced fleet for oceanography in the world.

Everyone is now talking in terms of deep research vehicles which will dive deeper, and longer, and be configured to perform real work. The interesting thing about deep research vehicles and development is that

[4]

although it was a talking point for so many years in concept, the idea was to build something that would go deeper, or do something more dramatic than its predecessor. We have actually found myriad calls for all kinds of real work and have discovered many ways that these vehicles can be useful.

Business has entered oceanography in several areas where it would have been impossible before. For several years industry was restricted to fabricating instruments and putting out perhaps a little better instrument; now we find that industry is capable of making surveys, conducting research and development programs in oceanography and generally coming into its own—developing the oceans for real profit. Twenty years ago, it would have been very difficult to find more than a half dozen industries in the United States which could have called themselves involved in any way in oceanography. Today the latest census lists over twenty-five hundred industries of various types concerned to some extent in oceanography, whether interested in manufacturing or actually capable of manning laboratories and ships, and training operators, research people and technicians to do any particular kind of oceanography required.

Twenty years ago, there were two schools in the United States offering degrees in oceanography; the latest publication of the Interagency Committee on Oceanography will probably list about eighty schools offering some kind of curriculum in the marine sciences. Last year I received over ten thousand letters, some admittedly from students saying "My

[5]

term paper is due tomorrow, I'm desperate, please tell me everything you know about oceanography." Some extend to valid questions such as "What is there in the ocean for *me*?" and "How can I make a legitimate profit out of the ocean?" These are the very encouraging letters that the federal agencies would like to receive.

Institutions appear to have increased in importance to the oceanographer. First of all, several centers of ocean technology are developing now. I might characterize them better as self-enclosed campuses where federal agencies and university laboratories co-exist in a very worthwhile relationship, sharing common facilities, libraries and computer centers. Industrial parks are now coming into the picture, and we find that sophisticated oceanographic concerns in various pockets of the country (on all three coasts incidentally) are capable of turning out some very advanced ocean technology. At the same time, the emphasis on training is now tending slightly towards the engineering and technician-training side, not supplanting scientific oceanography, but complementing it.

There is now a growing internationalism in oceanography, the basic principle of which is that if you cannot get along in the common playground of the ocean, however will you look forward later to getting along in one another's backyard? Dr. Maxwell will certainly elaborate on this.

Professional societies have grown tremendously;

twenty years ago the oceanographer could expect to join the oceanography section of the American Geophysical Union. Today the oceanographer emerging from school is confronted by a kaleidoscope of societies, associations, and sections of other societies, all professing to emphasize the study and the utilization of the oceans. This is not all good, because it dilutes the whole effort and the public image becomes somewhat blurred. For at least the time being, however, it is drawing more and more attention to the oceans and of course this is what we want. Thus, oceanographic history is advancing rapidly, and we look forward to some golden decades ahead.

Those of you who have been in this business have noticed that the government has been quite generous in supporting basic oceanographic research in several laboratories and universities throughout the country. When this research brings about an end in sight—a mission, a practical application—normally this will be contained within one of perhaps fifty to eighty government laboratories.

As one becomes a little older, in a few cases perhaps even slightly richer, his political persuasion will tend somewhat toward the right. Inevitably one wonders where is the proper cut-off for the competition between the federal laboratories and the private sector of the economy: the university laboratories and the industrial laboratories? This is a difficult determination.

Apparently, Congress recognizes this to some degree and last year passed, and the President signed

# NATIONAL PROGRAM IN
# OCEAN SCIENCE

into law last October, Public Law #89–566, the National Sea Grant College and Programs Act. This Act, one of the broadest charters that Congress has ever given the executive branch of government in federal aid programs, now allows the federal agency complex to support applied research and engineering technology in private laboratories.

Although the Act itself allows support of any kind of research, there is no question but that the intent of the Act, judging from hearings and congressional reports, is to emphasize applied research.

Philosophically we confront two basic principles in federal aid. First of all, one wants to get the best job done. One therefore goes to that group most capable of doing it. On the other hand, there is naturally a desire to provide aid where aid is most needed. Of course, these two concepts are not always compatible. So the Act itself has been divided, for the purpose of implementation, into Sea Grant Institutional support and Sea Grant Project support.

If a private group of any kind wants to carry out some kind of a training program, whether it be technician training, engineering training or other programs, these are tasks which are called sea grant projects. If the group wants to carry out applied research or some engineering project devoted to fisheries, mining, recreation, drugs from the sea, pollution control, this would be a sea grant project. If the group wants to carry out some kind of extension program, a

[8]

ABEL

training course, night courses, workshops, demonstrations, projects, these are sea grant projects.

When a college or private organization desires to mount a broad attack on all sectors of ocean technology, bringing in the training aspects and research aspects, this then is termed sea grant college activity and would merit Sea Grant Institutional support. We want to develop some kind of a balanced program, in a way resembling its cousin, the Land Grant Program, except that rather than being oriented to development of food from nature, this covers a broader spectrum including mining, recreation, etc. It is a very small program. We have, of course, high hopes for the future, and at the moment the National Science Foundation, which is in charge of implementation, has one million dollars of re-programmed money with four million expected for the next year.

I was asked to draw a note for the future and in order to do it very briefly, I should like to present it by way of a parable. Last year Mr. Clotworthy and I were invited to address the Third Space Science Congress. We went without an idea in our heads of what an ocean-oriented person says to space technologists. The day before the talk they took us through the Kennedy Moon Center. It is really incomparable, and thereupon we received our great vision of the future. The way I presented it to the space technologists was this: that in perhaps three or four years, depending upon how things work out, the largest doors in the whole world are going to open up in the largest building in the world and from these doors will emerge

[9]

the largest skyrocket ever conceived by the mind of man. It will roll ponderously up on the largest launching pad in the world, and take off with a roar which will make Vesuvius seem like a firecracker. In about three weeks this thing will return to the greatest reception ever given by man for man and from it will emerge the first man on the moon. In his hand he will have a rock . . . and when the American public realizes that they paid thirty-nine billion dollars for that rock, then my friends, we are going to have a national oceanography program!

### QUESTIONS

*Question:* How does our oceanographic program stack up against the Soviet program at this time?

*Mr. Abel:* There is no single answer to this question because the spectrum is as broad as the ocean technology itself. In some areas I really believe that the United States is well ahead. There are certain specialties. For instance, after World War II the Russians developed Arctic technology far in advance of ours. Where we would send a team of perhaps two or three people to the Arctic, they could have teams of fifty people studying, because it was very important to them. I have heard the statement that our first trip under the ice on the Nautilus gathered more oceanographic data than all previous cruises put together, so you can see it is a leapfrog kind of thing.

In fisheries, as Dr. Schaefer could probably explain far better than I, I have been given to understand that they have maybe fifty ships in the water conducting fisheries research; according to the Chief of their Bureau of Commercial Fisheries, Dr. Baghdanov, they can add another fifty to one hundred ships which are actually fishing but are equipped for fisheries research. This is a vast array of power to give science.

In physical oceanography, I suspect (and here I am open to argument from any quarter), that our exploits are probably exceeded by no country in the world. Several countries, of course, have applied specialties to their own particular needs; for instance, the Japanese have always been ahead in fishing technology. The French for a while were without peers in undersea exploration. But, broadly speaking, we have a fleet of perhaps eighty or ninety oceanographic vessels. There are something like six hundred or seven hundred students enrolled in oceanography curricula in schools. There is a vast amount of work in oceanography going on in this country. The budget, according to the President's report, totals nearly one-half billion dollars. In its aggregate reach, I really doubt (and this is only an opinion), that there is any other country possessing this broad aspect of power in the ocean.

*Question:* Has big business taken seriously to oceanography?
*Mr. Abel:* There are generally two principles by which industry goes into oceanography. A few indus-

tries which have started in ocean technology, have
progressed in ocean technology, and have made a good
living in oceanography. There are several other very
large industries, and I think you can include all of the
very largest industries in the United States, which
have in one way or another acquired an oceanographic
arm, either because they really believe that they can
utilize ocean technology right now, or in some cases
because they do not want to be caught napping if
certain kinds of industrial breakthrough occur.

*Question:* Will it be something like the Land Grant
Act of the 80's?
*Mr. Abel:* That is partly right. The sea grant bill
will not establish institutions from the ground up. It
will aid those already in being. We intend to issue a
detailed publication advising those interested in how
to subscribe to the sea grant program—how they can
participate in it. Generally speaking, it is quite con-
ventional in that one applies for support, sending
proposals for research or education. As we see the program developing now, the smaller schools will be coming
in for sea grant project support when they possess a
specific expertise concerning some kind of problem peculiar either to their geographical position or to an
industrial aspect of technology which has grown remarkably. Thus they would have aid in developing
their potential. The larger schools are already
equipped with this kind of power and they will be
coming in for perhaps broader support.

# ABEL

*Question:* What is the budget for the Sea Grant Colleges?

*Mr. Abel:* The act authorized five million dollars for 1967 and fifteen million dollars for 1968. The President's budget was zero for 1967 and four million dollars for 1968, but one million dollars of the National Science Foundation's own funds were allowed for reprogramming so that there are one million dollars now. Of the four million dollars requested of the Congress for 1968, the best understanding I have is that probably the entire four million dollars will in fact be appropriated. For 1969 it is impossible to say. Judging from the response to the issuance of the proclamations there is no doubt of the interest of the scientific and industrial communities. Apparently there is something about the concept of sea grant colleges which has so captured the imaginations of deans, college presidents and vice presidents, governors, senators and congressmen, that it almost resembles the drive of the lemmings to the sea. Naturally, this is very delightful. It is something we want to nurture and help grow if indeed this program is to be as successful as its perpetrators hope.

*Question:* In the scientific and academic community which are the kinds of scientists most needed?

*Mr. Abel:* Engineers and technicians. Again I am simply judging from the various projects and programs that the Interagency Committee on Oceanography fostered.

*Question:* Where is training in oceanography given?

# NATIONAL PROGRAM IN
# OCEAN SCIENCE

*Mr. Abel:* There are several institutions on all three coasts. The first two institutions offering degrees were the University of Washington, in Seattle, and what is known as the Scripps Institution of Oceanography, now part of the University of California. They have been offering degrees in oceanography and have carried strong graduate programs in oceanography for at least three decades. The Woods Hole Oceanographic Institution was the third of this triumvirate. This was started in the early 1930's with financial assistance from Rockefeller. Now, there are several large complexes of oceanography around the country. I will simply suggest a few. Starting at the Northeast, the Massachusetts Institute of Technology and Woods Hole certainly are very powerful centers of oceanography; the University of Rhode Island, the Lamont Geological Observatory of Columbia University and New York University (which has been specializing in meteorology and oceanology for many years). Others are Duke University (in Marine Biology), and the University of Miami (certainly one of the half dozen largest), and Texas A & M. The University of California, Oregon State University, and Johns Hopkins are all offering strong programs in oceanography. These have been established almost entirely at the graduate level, with the exception of the University of Washington. The intent here is fairly clear: the student is expected to obtain a strong background in one of the basic sciences, whether it be physics, chemistry, geology, biology, or engineering, at an accredited school. In obtaining his master's degree he normally encompasses basic courses in physical oceanography, chemical oceanography, marine biology, and submarine geology, and then for his doctorate he returns to his basic interests, and applies the second to the first. That is, now he blends his basic science with oceanography and does his research in that aspect of oceanography wherein is his basic skill.

*Question:* Are scientists in other fields who have turned to the sea as useful as scientists trained specifically in oceanography?

*Mr. Abel:* This is very pertinent. The history of oceanography has been most dramatically carried forward not by people with degrees in oceanography, but by chemists who turned their talents to the sea, by biologists who became marine biologists, and by physicists who went into problems of circulations of the sea. Someone on that committee once told me that of the third committee on oceanography of the National Academy of Science, not one had his own degree in oceanography. It is just as important to have a competent scientist in another field enter the lists of the oceanographers as it is to have the person coming up all the way in oceanography. Otherwise you do not have the proper cross fertilization; certainly so many of the problems in the ocean are so like those on land that the transference is easy.

Secondly, the problems are sufficiently complicated and sophisticated that it takes a degree of previous concentration in that science to apply to them. There is room for everyone with any kind of a strong scientific background.

[15]

# II

# OCEANOLOGY AND LEGISLATION

Fitzhugh Green, M.A.

*Special Assistant to Senator Claiborne Pell*

Oceanology, almost by definition, is an interdisciplinary subject. Those who enter the field soon find themselves surrounded by others of every background, with only their interest in the ocean itself as a common denominator. It is not surprising, therefore, that the national Congress, which represents every walk of American life, can today show such a uniformly strong interest in oceanology.

Still, at the moment, little significant legislation on oceanology is before the Congress. The reason is that legislators in both Houses are waiting for the National Council on Marine Resources and Engineering Development and the President's Commission on Marine Sciences to complete their thinking on America's future in oceanology.

The only kinds of oceanology legislation currently on the docket are bills to take care of fishermen's needs and other ocean problems that might arise, like the disastrous oil spillage from the tanker Torrey Canyon. In fact, means are now under study to forestall such events in advance. Almost on the day Congress began to think about this, a large oil slick appeared off Cape Cod and another off the Jersey Coast, so the problem is already as real for us as for the British.

[16]

As for the future, we can expect the principal legislative action to be based on the blueprint and recommendations of the Presidential Marine Sciences Commission.

The 89th Congress' two most significant laws to advance America in oceanology were the Magnuson Act, which established the Council and Commission just cited, and the Pell Sea Grant College and Program Act. The Pell Act is designed to speed our country's capability in marine science and technology through programs of practical training, applied research and information activity—to spread new technologic knowledge wherever it can be used.

Since all of you here will at one time or another have ideas that should be translated into law, it is certainly appropriate to give you a brief picture of how to get an oceanology bill through Congress. I will use Senator Pell's Sea Grant College Act as a prime example. Here is how he brought it from a mere suggestion to law in an astonishingly short period:

In 1963 the brilliant, imaginative South African who had become Dean of the University of Minnesota's Institute of Technology—Athelstan Spilhaus—conceived the idea of a sea grant college program. In his own individualistic approach to science and politics, he saw a philosophic parallel between the need to develop our marine resources today and the need of a newer nation, in 1862, to develop its agricultural resources. Senator Justin Morrill of Vermont spawned land grant colleges over a hundred years ago; Senator Pell of Rhode Island, a man attuned to the sea and its

[17]

# OCEANOLOGY AND LEGISLATION

possibilities, produced the Sea Grant College Bill in 1965.

There are certain guidelines to winning passage of any Federal legislation, and Senator Pell knows them well. The first is to enlist a constituency, both inside and outside of the Congress, which will support the bill; and the second is to keep on top of the bill endlessly until the President signs it into law.

Having introduced S-2439, for Sea Grant Colleges and Programs, Senator Pell hastened to build a constituency. He participated in a conference on the sea grant college concept in Newport, Rhode Island. The conference took place in October, 1965, under the auspices of the University of Rhode Island and the Southern New England Marine Sciences Association. Over 200 participants came from thirty states around the nation. Publicity, and refinement of the concept itself, resulted. Athelstan Spilhaus, Senator Pell, and many key figures in oceanologic circles elaborated on the idea's great potential. Afterwards, articles appeared in various magazines, and a book by Senator Pell and Harold L. Goodwin, *Challenge of the Seven Seas,* highlighted the sea grant concept.

Senator Pell moved early the following spring to set up hearings.

To draw further on New England regional support developed at the Newport conference, Pell held the first hearing, on May 1, at the University of Rhode Island (URI). Leaders from URI and other focal points of oceanologic activity warmly endorsed the bill. The hearing was keynoted by President Francis Horn,

under whom URI's Graduate School of Oceanography
has become one of the nation's best.

In Washington, three more days of hearings turned
up still more support in testimony heard and read
from scores of experts.

The hearings ended May 4. The next move was to
secure the Administration's approval, or at least
agreement not to contest the bill. This routine is common to the party in power. It makes sense because the
Bureau of the Budget (BuBud) can make obstacles
later by not asking for an appropriation. Congress,
in turn, can insist and vote money anyway, but this is
a route the Congress rarely follows and likes to avoid
if possible.

At the time we went to BuBud, its sentiment was
running against oceanology. The Magnuson Bill (for
an overall new look at the nation's future in oceanology) was receiving neither endorsement nor per-
missiveness from the White House. The latter was all
Senator Pell sought. He talked directly to one senior
White House assistant who liked the sea grant plan.
He also liked the oceanology theme itself and predicted that White House bureaucracy soon would turn
in favor of it. He was right, as events soon proved.

Professional BuBud staffers worked on the bill.
After several lengthy consultations, and a number of
language and substantive suggestions, they consented
to write a letter stating BuBud had no objections.

The letter arrived only hours before the subcom-
mittee's first mark-up of the bill. This is an executive
session wherein a bill is chiseled and honed into what

[19]

should be its final form in the Senate. In preparation we furnished an abstract of the bill's purpose and a copy of BuBud's letter, and held "pretrial" discussions with assistants of the member senators.

At a second mark-up session unanimous approval moved the bill to the full Committee on Labor and Public Welfare.

The next step was procedural: to get on the agenda of the upcoming meeting. There is an unwritten mystique about when full committee meetings are held and what bills win a place on the agenda. Timing is difficult, as it always is for senators.

As a neophyte on the scene, I was worried; and the committee's general counsel, though helpful in every way, was not sanguine either. He warned the bill probably could not be enacted in one session even though it was not controversial. Senator Pell publicly would say only that he was hopeful. Privately, he never ceased pushing, telephoning, writing notes and letters, and making personal contacts wherever his intercession seemed needed.

Pell was now uneasy about Sea Grant's fate in the House. Already some twenty "companion" (identical) bills had been introduced by representatives. Like S. 2439, they amended the National Science Foundation Act and were hence referred to the House Committee on Science and Astronautics. But no action was being taken. They lay clustered on the committee's table, unscheduled and unmoving, with a future about as dynamic as a barnacle's.

By the time the Labor and Public Welfare Com-

mittee had met on June 24 and unanimously reported
S. 2439, Senator Pell had formed his strategy with
respect to House action. At this point I saw clearly
how the two houses of Congress must and do work
independently of each other. Nevertheless, with the
normal deference between members of the respective
houses and a worthy bill to work with, common cause
can be found. Sea Grant was such a bill.

Paul Rogers (Fla.), an articulate, hard-driving
enthusiast for oceanology, was the House figure on
whom Senator Pell based his plan. The idea was that,
under Rogers' leadership, a bill could be moved
through the Merchant Marine Committee and the full
House; and that the Senate could then pass this bill
as its own. Otherwise the Pell Bill would, if passed by
the Senate, go directly to the Science and Astronautics
Committee, where it would doubtless wither like the
House bills already there.

Pell's joint scheme with Rogers operated well, in
the following way:

Rogers speedily staged a one-day hearing which,
added to the four days of Senate hearings, provided
enough in the Record to go ahead.

The vigorous team of Rogers, Garmatz and Lennon
saw to it that Rogers' bill, H.R. 16559, was soon
reported favorably.

Then the Rules Committee, which controls traffic
in the House, came into the picture and for a short
while clouded it with delay. At last the signal turned
green, and H.R. 16559 was slated for an early vote.

Like expectant fathers, Robert Smith, Rogers' assistant, and I sat poised in the House gallery on the appointed day in August for several hours, while Congressman Rogers served as floor manager in the chamber below. Unfortunately, the House adjourned without acting, and we retreated to our respective tents with disappointment. But victory came a month later. On September 13, the House unanimously adopted the sea grant concept. Just before the vote, Congressman H. R. Gross (Iowa) frightened us for a moment with what seemed to be an attack; but his question proved innocuous.

In the senior legislative chamber, Senator Pell was ready. Clued to the exact moment of its arrival from the House, Pell rose and asked unanimous consent that H.R. 16559 be stripped of all after its enacting clause and the language of S. 2439 be substituted. There was no objection, and H.R. 16559 returned to the House as the Rogers Bill but in the Pell Bill form. The date was September 14.

This Senate action seemed easy. It took only two or three minutes plus the time required for laudatory remarks by Senator Wayne Morse (Ore.). It happened so simply on the surface that for a moment it was hard to remember all Senator Pell's behind-the-scenes planning, campaigning and obtaining the Democratic leadership's help in scheduling Sea Grant.

The next move, to request a joint House-Senate conference to sort out differences between the House and Senate versions, was up to the House. It was prompt in coming because Rogers, like Pell, had done his homework well.

GREEN

The bills now had more than two dozen differences. The main one was due to the passage in June of the National Marine Resources and Engineering Development Act of 1966 (the Magnuson Bill, which had at last received White House support). The House had accordingly revised its original companion bill to amend the new Magnuson Act (instead of the Merchant Marine Act). It also stipulated that policy oversight be given by the Magnuson Act Council headed by the Vice President instead of a separate, non-governmental panel of experts in the original Pell Bill.

At staff level we tried to resolve this and other differences in advance of the conference. Most of the changes were refinements which made for more flexibility and so were acceptable. But the conference proved to be something of a cliffhanger, mostly because the conferees had so much to say. We were fearful that time would run out—it was now October 4, and Sea Grant would have to take a long winter sleep until the next session.

The setting was in E-100, one of the Capitol's most ornately decorated rooms. Attendance was almost 100 percent. It was an executive session with no outsiders present. But what promised in advance to be a ratification in a few minutes of staff accord became hours long. Clearly each legislator wanted to add his own touch to make the Sea Grant Program not only a new departure in oceanology, but one that would be perfect in every detail. Finally they were satisfied with their creation and voted it into being.

# OCEANOLOGY AND LEGISLATION

On October 15, President Lyndon B. Johnson signed the National Sea Grant College and Program Act of 1966. Thus, in a remarkably swift time an entirely new kind of ocean-regulated legislation had been brought from just a wish at the start of hearings on May 1 to the law of the land on October 15.

Briefly, the reasons seemed to be: First, the temper of Congress and the country was pro-oceanologic development. Whether due to fear of an underwater Sputnik, or curiosity, or the hope of vast as yet undiscovered riches from the sea, Americans were happy to spend millions of dollars to shine a bright light in the dark shadows of inner space. The total federal oceanology budget for fiscal year 1968 called for $462 million. The White House shift in favor of oceanology which helped speed passage of the Magnuson Act was another reason. A third was Senator Pell himself. Although the bill's ultimate passage was never seriously challenged, it was beset by constant roadblocks. They stemmed from the intense competition for time and money in the Congress.

The Senator himself followed every tiny twist and turn on the bill's trip through the legislative alimentary canal. Frequent obstacles threatened to delay adoption at least until the 90th Congress. Without Senator Pell's daily, energetic drive to win enactment in 1966—during his own campaign for reelection—the bill would never have become statute that year.

Hundreds of telephone calls, letters, notes, and personal contacts were involved. Yet the efforts would have been fruitless without the respect and liking Pell has won in both Houses. There were many Senators and Congressmen who smoothed the way, particularly Magnuson, who initially agreed to allow Sea Grant to go to the committee on which Pell served; and Rogers, who gave great dollops of leadership and cooperation in the House.

It was a feat nonetheless. Now the same ingredients will be needed to assure adequate appropriations and continuity for the program when its statutory limit ends next year.

I would like to close with a plea to all of you: that you add a new habit to your thinking in oceanology—that you practice working together as a growing and vital constituency which will make its ideas felt in the Congress through your letters, your lectures and speeches and books and articles. The handful of really knowledgeable experts in oceanology are the unsung heroes in the Sea Grant College Bill's success story. That was a claque that clicked. I urge you all to join that claque for more and more achievement along America's march into sea-mastery.

*Comment by Dr. Sammartino:* I find it very thrilling that school administrators, scientists, persons in business, lawyers and legislators all work together on what I feel is the new and the last frontier for the United States and for every other country. I think that most people do not realize that the sea is not as big as we once conceived it, and that this is our last frontier. Now our progress depends on whether nations can cooperate in the use of the sea or whether we are all going our separate ways. For instance, to mention just the international legislative aspect, we have not been able to get agreement on that. Some of us think of the three mile limit, some of the nations think of the six mile limit; others have a twelve mile limit and some nations have a two hundred mile limit. Now what is it going to be? It seems to me that we have two problems: we have the problem of oceanology as it affects our own nation, and we have the larger problem as it affects the interdependence of various nations in the use of the sea. There is no one who cannot go out in the middle of the ocean and stake out an empire if he can do something with it. We have catapulted over the ocean problem into the space problem. It would be my hope that somehow a sense of balance could be established in this country, and we could give the problems of the sea the importance that they deserve.

QUESTIONS

*Question:* Do the agricultural colleges participate in the exploitation of the food from the sea program?
*Mr. Green:* I think one related point that is going to come out as the conversation continues is that while we are farmers on land we are still hunters in the sea. The answer to your question is yes. I believe several of the colleges that are active in oceanography are in fact land grant colleges. An example is the University of Rhode Island, whose Graduate School of Oceanography is one of the best half dozen in the nation.

*Question:* What role does UNESCO play in the development of the sea, particularly from the international standpoint?

*Mr. Green:* The United Nations is involved in oceanology in several ways. There is the International Maritime Consultative Organization which concerns itself with shipping matters, including oil pollution. Last year the General Assembly passed a United States resolution introduced by former Congressman James Roosevelt of California, to have the Secretary General launch an international study in oceanography, and report back to the General Assembly this year. Then there is the Food and Agriculture Organization (FAO). The FAO is busy with the question of living resources of the world in general, and fisheries especially. The UNESCO itself harbors an Intergovernmental Oceanographic Committee on Oceanography (IOC), whose membership includes 52 nations. IOC's activities are science-oriented, and it has sponsored the Indian Ocean Expedition and other investigations under SCOR— the UN's Scientific Committee on Ocean Research. As to IOC's role, Senator Pell said in his book, *Challenge of the Seven Seas,* that "with proper support and leadership it could become the principal international motivator and coordinator of governmental cooperation."

*Question:* What is the relationship between ESSA and the Sea Grant College Program?

*Mr. Green:* ESSA is the Environmental Science Services Administration of the Department of Commerce. They caused a great deal of furor in the past few months when they announced they would soon move their institute of oceanology from Washington, D.C., to a more appropriate site on the East Coast. Suddenly it became apparent that there were 115 sites that considered themselves as the perfect place for the institute to move. ESSA thus kindled much new interest in oceanology. In fact, towns who have never talked as a whole community before suddenly found themselves vigorous and united proponents for oceanologic expansion!

Actually the Sea Grant College Program has nothing directly to do with ESSA's Insitute of Oceanography. Still the Pell Sea Grant Act does call for appropriate borrowing on a reimbursable basis of facilities and people from anywhere in the Federal Government.

*Question:* Is it a good idea for the United Nations to consider the whole question of jurisdiction and ownership in the extraterritorial seas?

*Mr. Green:* This is a question that will not get a straight answer from anyone in the Executive Branch at this time, because there are so many considerations that have not been worked out. But I believe that the United Nations members should jointly discuss the problems that we are forced to face on ownership and jurisdiction beyond the territorial limit and continental shelf. As it stands today, ocean space outside the control of national sovereignty can become a tremendous trouble area. Already marine technology has made it possible to operate in the deep ocean where no man could venture before. As technology continues to improve and more people from more nations increase their efforts to explore and exploit this new frontier, difficult legal confrontations are bound to occur. Certainly the United Nations should play a helpful role when the nations that will be concerned start negotiating toward a legal regime to avoid chaos under the high seas.

*Question:* Can you tell us how much the Russians are doing in oceanology?

*Mr. Green:* When I was in the United States Information Agency, we never really knew how much the Soviet Union spent on propaganda. We made some healthy estimates which we thought would help in our budget submissions to Congress, but we were never completely sure, and certainly are not sure in the field of oceanology either. Nevertheless, it seems likely they are more active than any country besides the United States.

There is one good thing that any oceanologist knows to be true: there is more freedom and flexibility in exchanges between our oceanologists and theirs, compared to other USSR-US scientific exchanges. This seems the most friendly arena, and there is even some joint activity. For example, during the time of the Cuban blockade when our Navy was parading up and down off the shores of Cuba, I understand that our oceanologists were meeting at sea with oceanologists from Soviet ships—in another part of the ocean, of course.

*Question:* Is the exploration of oil properties under the seas a department or a branch of oceanology?
*Mr. Green:* Yes, I believe you call such activity marine geology.

*Question:* How do you limit the territorial rights? How far out do our territorial rights go in digging for oil under the sea?
*Mr. Green:* Under the Geneva Convention, I understand you can go out to a depth of two hundred meters or as far as you can effectively exploit the resources on the bottom, or under it.

# III

# FOOD FROM THE SEA

Milner B. Schaefer, Ph.D.

*Director, Institute of Marine Resources, University of California at San Diego*

Gifford Pinchot, early in this century, invented the term "conservation." This led to a great deal of public attention and debate, somewhat the way oceanography or oceanology, or whatever you call it, does now. Some years thereafter President McKinley remarked that it seems that there are a great many people in this country who are in favor of conservation, no matter what it means. Perhaps we are in somewhat the same situation with regard to oceanography. There are a number of folks, and I am one of the guilty parties, who in the last decade or two, called to the public's attention, and to the legislators', some of the uses of the ocean that could perhaps provide increased benefits to mankind. This has struck a responsive note, in juxtaposition to the demands, generated by the population explosion, for food, minerals and other resources. A large number of people are getting extremely interested in oceanography, or oceanology. I shall use the term oceanography, having been indoctrinated in it.

There are indeed a great many riches out in the ocean; they are also very difficult to get out of the ocean. They will not jump into the boat.

Food from the sea is a very important resource. It

[31]

# FOOD FROM THE SEA

has been considered, among other food sources, in a new study by a Committee of the President's Scientific Advisory Council on the World Food Problem, two volumes of which have just been released to the public. A great many people are concerned with the problem of matching up the food supplies and the growing population in the world. In the paper that I have prepared for this conference, I attempt to consider the role of food from the sea, in relation to the global food problem, in a realistic fashion, and to discuss some of the important problems involved in harvesting the sea's living resources.

President Johnson in his State of the Union message on January 10, 1967, said, "Next to the pursuit of peace, the really greatest challenge to the human family is the race between food supply and population increase. That race tonight is being lost." This desperate race has attracted much attention from natural and social scientists, government administrators, industrialists, etc. All seem to have their own pet answers. These range from the overriding necessity of an all-out drive for birth control, to prevent further increase in the human population, to assertions that any one of several potential sources of food can easily support a human population many times that now inhabiting this planet. The sources, each of which is supposed to be able easily to feed the burgeoning human population, include improved agriculture, raising of yeasts and other microbiota on materials produced through plant culture, growing of such micro-organisms on petroleum substrates, and, of course, the "unlimited" food supply of the ocean. It is my purpose here to consider this latter source.

In the first place, I think that we can all agree that it is not possible for the human population to continue to increase indefinitely, because the resources of this planet, however large they may be, are finite and thus, *a fortiori,* can support only a finite population, however large. Moreover, the preservation of adequate quality of life must become overwhelmingly important long before we reach the absolute upper physical limit to the human population. In the shorter term, there is the critical problem of improving the per capita incomes of people in the underdeveloped nations. This requires an economic growth rate larger than the population growth rate. Thus, curtailment of the rate of human reproduction is certainly of outstanding importance. However, even with the most vigorous efforts in this direction, the present population of the world will almost certainly double before we reach a steady state of reproduction in balance with mortality, and that level of population (about six billion people) is to be expected by the end of this century. We have adequately to feed six billion people. It is in this context that I will examine the possible role of the living resources of the sea.

The ocean is a very poor place to look to for the food-energy requirements of humanity. This is because food energy (calories) is most easily obtainable from plants, which are much better grown on land. Except for the large algae along the shallow seacoast, the plants of the sea are mostly tiny microscopic phyto-

# FOOD FROM THE SEA

plankton, existing in small standing crops, with rapid turnover rates, quite infeasible to harvest on any reasonable economic basis. Fortunately, high calorie vegetable foods are easily grown on the land. The really critical factor in the nutrition of our present population is protein, and especially the high quality protein, obtainable from animal sources, that is an essential part of the human diet, and for lack of which at least a quarter of the present human population suffers serious physical and mental retardation. Let us, then, look at the protein requirements, and the possibility of satisfying them from the ocean. The total protein requirement is about eighty grams per capita per day, including a requirement for high-grade (animal) protein of fifteen grams per capita per day. Six billion people will require about $1.8 \times 10^8$ tons per year of total protein, including about $3.2 \times 10^7$ tons of animal protein. These requirements correspond to about 1200 million and 219 million tons of fish, respectively.

As I have shown elsewhere (Schaefer 1965, and 1968) even the larger requirement is available for sustainable harvest from the sea, at the level of first stage carnivores. However, considering economic and other factors, I have also estimated that a harvest of two hundred million tons of fish per year is rather easily attainable, without any spectacular new technological developments and this, as we have seen, could provide the full requirement of animal protein for twice as many people as now exist on this planet. This

[34]

would require quadrupling the present harvest from the sea, and using it all to feed directly to people.

Turning next to the problem of how to obtain the harvest from the sea, I would like first to deal with aquaculture, or fish farming, which has been recently so highly touted both in the scientific and lay literature. While fish farming in enclosed or semi-enclosed portions of the sea, or employing sessile organisms in the open sea along the coast, has considerable potential for producing luxury products of high unit value, it has little application to the problem of providing thirty million tons of inexpensive animal protein to six billion people of average low income, or even providing the necessary animal protein to the poor and hungry millions among the present three billion population. This is because the cost of producing animal protein by aquaculture cannot hope to be competitive in the reasonably foreseeable future with the harvesting of the wild stocks of the ocean, that can sustain a very large harvest at very low cost under appropriate, rather simple, conservation management. The real potential of the sea consists of organisms, low in the food chain, such as sardines and anchovies, that can be strained out of the water in large quantities at low cost. This kind of fish is now being landed in Peru at less than $15 a ton, in California at about $20 a ton, on the U. S. Atlantic coast at about $30 a ton, and elsewhere in the world at similar prices. Many of the stocks of these organisms are only beginning to be utilized, and others, such as the large stock of sardines in the Arabian Sea, are essentially not being used at

# FOOD FROM THE SEA

all. Neither aquaculture nor animal husbandry can approach this raw material price. For example, chicken is being produced at prices approximately $200 to $250 a ton (about equal to the landed cost of tuna, which is a very high-priced fish) under very efficient and intensive animal husbandry. Pigs and cows run somewhat higher. Oysters, clams, mussels, shrimp, mullet and milkfish, anadromous fish such as salmon, plaice, and all of the other organisms that are being widely touted as objects of aquaculture are not going to be produced at less than $100 a ton for yet a very long time, if ever.

It is interesting to note that the most rapidly growing sector of the marine fisheries is for these abundant clupeid and engraulid fishes and their relatives. While the world harvest of the living resources of the sea, during the decade 1955–65, approximately doubled from 24.5 to 45.3 million tons, the catch of this group of fishes approximately tripled from 6.3 to 17.5 million tons, and now constitutes about 40 percent of the total world harvest. Nearly all of the increase in harvest of this group of organisms, low in the food chain, is being used for the production of fish meal which is routed to human beings via animal feed stuffs, a large share being lost in the process. This is, of course, much more desirable than letting the fish go to waste, and the efficiency of transfer through chickens, swine and cattle is undoubtedly higher than efficiency of transfer through halibut or tuna, but direct utilization by human beings would be, obviously, even more efficient.

How, then, may we extract two hundred million or more tons of fish and other marine organisms and get them to human beings efficiently and effectively? The answer involves problems not only in marine biology and oceanography, but also important social and political problems.

From the standpoint of the natural sciences, it is obvious that we should continue the development of the means of harvesting and utilizing the organisms low in the food chain, including not only the kinds of fishes I have already mentioned, but others, such as the myctophids and deep sea smelts, and other organisms such as the krill in the Antarctic and their relatives elsewhere. In regard to the Antarctic krill, Russian oceanographers and food scientists are even now conducting experiments which, if successful, could lead to a continuing harvest of some one hundred million tons per year.

Secondly, the ability of modern technology rapidly to exploit even a very large fish population can lead to its being overfished within a few years unless appropriate conservation measures are taken. Such measures require intensive scientific research from the outset, to provide the factual basis for correct conservation management. Since the exploited species may, in at least some cases, be closely coupled with other species in the same area, techniques of conservation management need to take into account not only the management of the fishery on the exploited species-population, but also the effects on its competitors and predators. A notable example of how this has been done very badly is the fishery off the coast of California that, because of institutional handicaps, was restricted essentially to the California sardine and was not allowed to be brought to bear on its close competitor, the anchovy. As a result of this and of over-fishing the sardine, it has disappeared economically, while the anchovy population has burgeoned, but is yet protected from being effectively harvested by California fishermen. We must consider the complex of resources in any given sea area, and adopt intelligent measures to realize the harvest thereof, including an appropriately balanced harvest of competing species, as well as control of "weed" species and of undesirable predators.

The next obvious need is for the development of more effective and efficient harvesting systems. This requires continued efforts of marine scientists for developing the understanding of the relation of the ocean to the distribution and behavior of its inhabitants, that engineers and fishermen can use for the improved design and deployment of fishing equipment. I have discussed some aspects of this elsewhere (Schaefer 1966). It also requires the application of advanced engineering and other technological methods, and especially of the application of systems analysis, an approach which, so far, has been largely neglected.

Development of additional food products that will be acceptable to consumers, yet inexpensive enough so they can afford to buy them, is perhaps an even more important problem for technology. The strong effort toward the development of fish protein concentrates as an element of the war on hunger is well-known to everyone. This is a highly important endeavor, but FPC is certainly not the only new product that should be developed.

The most important obstacles to the full utilization of the resources of the sea for the benefit of mankind are, however, not in the realm of the natural sciences and engineering, but in the realm of the social and political sciences, because some of the major handicaps are institutional. For example, we are seeing rapid growth of the jurisdictions of individual nations over increasingly large areas of the high seas, which may very well seriously handicap the effective utilization of the living resources. There are a great many legal restrictions, at the state and national levels, which impose unnecessary restraints on development of fishery products. Two examples are the restrictions by the Pure Food and Drug Administration on the manufacture and sale of fish protein concentrate made from whole fish, and the restriction by the State of California on the utilization of marine resources for the preparation of fish meal for animal husbandry.

Perhaps the most important set of institutional handicaps arises from the purposive imposition of inefficient harvesting methods. These arise because of the common property nature of the living resources of the sea, which, in some instances, leads to larger potential fishing effort than that corresponding to the optimum yield of the fishery resource. In addition to the resulting economic problems, due to over-capitalization, which have been widely discussed, there are

[39]

often imposed serious inefficiencies through legal measures. These are designed to make the fishing gear or fishing operations sufficiently inefficient to restrict the effective effort to that which the fish population can withstand, in the face of many more fishermen than are required for taking the harvest. Unless we can somehow overcome these and other institutional handicaps, our advances in science and technology will be largely frustrated.

### REFERENCES

Schaefer, M. B., "The Potential Harvest of the Sea." *Transactions,* American Fisheries Society, LXLIV, No. 2 (1965), 123–128.

_____,"Oceanography and the Marine Fisheries." North American Fisheries Conference, Washington, D.C., April 30–May 5, 1965. Washington, D.C.: Government Printing Office, 17–20 (1966).

_____, "Economic and Social Needs for Marine Resources," *Ocean Engineering,* ed. John F. Braktz. New York: Wiley, 1968.

### QUESTIONS

*Question:* In the Gulf of Mexico we have about five million acres of protected water, much of which is now producing oysters, water that could be used to raise shrimp, and for other kinds of mariculture. Is it not true that in Peru the anchovy population is greatly diminished by an oceanic catastrophe every four to seven years? What will such fluctuations do to the supply of fish protein concentrate made from such cheap fish?

*Dr. Schaefer:* I think mariculture is a very good bet for raising a great many kinds of fish; furthermore, I think your mariculture in the Gulf of Mexico is highly important, but I do not think you are going to produce fish for twenty dollars per ton, and I think we will be able to continue to do this with the lower trophic level wild populations.

As far as Peru is concerned, this fluctuation of anchovy abundance of four to seven years is not true. This was the story before we really found out. What really happens is that, in the years of warm surface water, called "El Niño," the fish go deep where the guano birds cannot get at them, so the guano birds take a beating. But the fish are still where the fishermen can catch them. The population stayed large and it continued to be harvested at the level of eight million tons during the last "El Niño" in 1965–66, and the stock is now in very good condition.

I think that fish protein concentrate, of whatever form, is going to have to be handled on a world-market basis exactly the way we do with fish meal for the poultry business. If it is a poor year in Peru, it may be good in the Arabian Sea; if you have a bad year off Norway, you have a good year off South Africa. We have to get away from the parochial business of saying, as the Gulf of Mexico goes, so goes the world, or as California goes, so goes the world. It simply is not true.

*Question:* Do you not believe that we will run out of wild fish populations that can be harvested cheaply, and that we will have to turn to mariculture?

*Dr. Schaefer:* I think I know where there are enough fish around the world, and enough up-coming technology, to continue to produce fish from these large wild stocks cheaper than you can raise them. I think that mariculture is very important for raising certain gourmet items, for getting a much larger yield-per-acre of them, and making a profit from them.

*Question:* Do you really believe that the wild fish populations can be expected to continue to hold up under fishing? Won't the fishing cause them to decline so that they can't provide a harvest?

*Dr. Schaefer:* Well, some of the stocks of North Atlantic herring have been exploited for about a thousand years, and they are holding up pretty well.

*Question:* What about our estuaries, that are important nursery grounds for the fisheries?

*Dr. Schaefer:* There is competition from the real estate development people who want to fill in estuaries for housing, factories or golf courses, as well as the need of space for garbage disposal by "sanitary fill." Using such areas for land fill competes with the use of the estuary as nursery grounds for the fisheries. This is one of the things that a recent study in California revealed, when our State Planning Office asked us to take an across-the-board look at the use of the ocean. We recommended that one of the most critical things to avoid is making such economically irreversible decisions, because once you fill a piece of an estuary, even though physically you might be capable of scooping it out later, economically it is irreversible.

*Question:* Are you familiar with marine algae, which can be produced in great quantities in a form which could be used as a food?

*Dr. Schaefer:* Yes. We have in California the leading fishery for kelp in the United States. The Kelco Company, in my hometown in the state of California, handles about one hundred thousand tons a year. I am familiar with this, and I agree with you on its possible food potential. My point is that the quantity of this is relatively small in relation to the food-energy demand of twenty-five hundred calories per day for each of six billion people, because it is only along the shallow margin of the sea where these fixed algae grow. They are important, but the quantity you can grow is relatively limited in relation to the carbohydrate demand of six billion people.

*Question:* Why do you say that it would be better to make fish protein concentrate for direct human consumption, than to use the fish meal as a diet supplement for chickens and other animals that people eat?

*Dr. Schaefer:* You see, what happens in the case of chickens: you feed chickens (that is, those grown by

[43]

modern procedures in the United States) a mixture of about four percent fish meal, or the equivalent, together with grain and you get, for about a pound and a half of the dry feed mix, a pound of chicken on the hoof. But in the whole process, when you finish counting all of the inputs—capital, labor, fish meal and everything else—the cost of chicken is about two hundred dollars, or two hundred and fifty dollars, per ton. From the standpoint of getting as much fish protein as possible into people, putting it through chickens is, of course, a perfectly good way of doing it. But fish-flour should cost only about twenty-five cents a pound at wholesale. Thus, at wholesale, it will be cheaper than the chicken. Since the chicken, at twelve cents a pound, is only fifteen percent protein, the price is around ninety cents per pound for pure protein, compared with about thirty cents a pound for that in fish-flour, which is eighty percent protein.

*Question:* William Paddock, in his book *Famine 1975,* says that although we have the technology to solve the problem, we, and this includes the whole world, will not be smart enough or quick enough to ward off the famine that he foresees for 1975. Do you agree with him?
*Dr. Schaefer:* It is hard to say. I am a bit of an optimist; I keep hoping that we will be smart enough to apply what we know.

*Question:* What do you think of the possibility of increasing the fertilization of the upper sunlit layer of the sea by pumping up deep, nutrient-rich water?

# SCHAEFER

*Dr. Schaefer:* We have looked at this. It is tied up with the cost of power. If we develop sufficiently cheap power, we might be able to use atomic power, or whatever else, as an energy source to move the deep-water fertilizer up to the surface. Using present atomic power sources, from the calculations we have made, it does not look very good; it is far too expensive.

*Question:* Wouldn't the pumping up of the deep water be attractive if it is put in a lagoon, so that the fertilizer is contained, and all gets used?

*Dr. Schaefer:* It is a possibility, I suppose, that you could pump up the water and put it in an enclosed, or semi-enclosed, basin so that you do not lose too much by diffusion. This becomes more attractive, but still not very good economically.

Another difficulty we have, and this is a big problem (the same problem as exists now in the Chesapeake Bay where we are already adding nutrients from processed sewage), is as follows: When you are farming corn, for example, it is monoculture. You are raising one kind of plant. You go out and plow the field; you plant corn seeds; you throw on a lot of fertilizer; the corn plants pop up, and so do a lot of weeds. But you can go out there with your cultivator and selectively knock down the weeds until the corn plants get high enough to get along by themselves. In the Chesapeake Bay, or the Great Lakes, we are putting in a lot of lovely fertilizer, and we have a whole big crop of plants, but we don't like them, and we don't know which ones we want. And we don't know how to select

[45]

or encourage those, if we did. Thus, the problem of fertilizing the sea is not quite so easy.

*Question:* Do you think we are going to be able to solve the problem of getting shellfish that is free from contamination?

*Dr. Schaefer:* Yes. We do it now, in fact. Most of our shellfish are marketed in pretty good condition. You have certain small odds on getting hepatitis from clams or oysters. You also have certain small odds on getting tapeworm from eating beefsteak if you like it extra rare. The Public Health Service is attempting to run a good inspection business. One thing, of course, which can be done to increase the supply of shellfish is to take them from contaminated beds and hold them in tanks, or other places where there is a flow of good clean water. After holding them for a certain time, they clear themselves.

*Question:* Is it not very important to manage the sea fisheries to conserve them; to keep them from being overfished?

*Dr. Schaefer:* Exactly. This happens to be my own specialty, looking at the dynamics of exploited populations. It is a matter essentially like range management. We have to manage the harvest of the fish, of the species or mixture of species, so that we can maintain the harvest at its maximum yield. We have to neither underfish nor overfish the stock.

*Question:* Can you do it? And why do we continue to make fish meal for fertilizer?

# SCHAEFER

*Dr. Schaefer:*  Yes, we can. In fact, even on the international scene there are a number of Commissions successfully doing so; for example, the International Pacific Salmon Fisheries Commission that handles the salmon fishery of the Fraser River; the International Halibut Commission in the North Pacific; the Inter-American Tropical Tuna Commission, that I was director of for a number of years and that is now regulating the yellowfin tuna fishery in the whole eastern Pacific, from California to Peru and far offshore. We can, very definitely, do this. But it requires a large research base, and, as we get more and more species into full production, we have to do these things more and more carefully.

In answer to your second question, on fish meal, there is very little fish meal that is used as fertilizer. In fact, it is practically all used as food for livestock. Years ago they used some as fertilizer, but now there are much cheaper sources of fertilizer. You can get a lot more for your fish meal if you sell it to the chicken farmers.

*Question:*  Can you tell us about how the Tuna Commission was developed in the Pacific?

*Dr. Schaefer:*  That particular international activity arose from the fact that the United States' tuna fishery had expanded considerably before World War II, and immediately after that war it had started expanding even faster. This is a tropical fishery, for yellowfin tuna and skipjack tuna, that was based largely in California, and was expanding rapidly down the Latin American coast. There was a controversy with some of

[47]

the Latin American countries, because some of them were worried about the possibility of overfishing these important tuna populations. So there was an international treaty drawn up, to establish a Commission that would employ a Director of Investigations, who would hire and supervise a scientific staff to investigate these things, and find out what the facts were, and then make recommendations for management, if necessary. It turned out we were pretty lucky. We started the investigations in 1951, and we found that none of the tuna populations (yellowfin or skipjack) was being overfished. We had an opportunity to continue to examine the tuna populations and the whole fishery in some detail, over quite a few years, until along about 1964 when the fishing effort reached just over the maximum yield point for yellowfin tuna. We then had a very good basis for recommendations for managing the yellowfin tuna fishery. The skipjack tuna population is way underfished yet, but the one species (yellowfin) requires management. It was put under conservation management last year.

IV

# HEALTH RESOURCES AND FOOD
# FROM THE SEA

## John H. Heller, M.D.

*President, New England Institute Graduate School*

Among scientists and thoughtful laymen it is now commonplace to say that the oceans offer vast potential sources of food, minerals, pharmaceuticals, and other substances to make life more worth living.

I have been asked to discuss food and health resources from the sea, and am concerned with two major factors. One is that in fields in which we are well informed we are not solving the problems when the solution is right before us now, and the other is how to go about solving some of the problems that we have not yet solved.

If the rise of the West, intellectually, scientifically and financially personified as one of the highest levels in the United States, and certainly, California not the least, has so-called institutional problems so that it cannot figure out what to overfish and what to conserve, you have right here, not the situation of the starving Indian population, where they are still using wooden plows, but you have among ourselves those who are not doing things correctly when a little common sense might dictate how it could be done infinitely better.

As to social implications, I am reminded of a major dairy producer who saw a huge amount of savan-

[49]

nah land ideal for cattle raising in South America. He inquired about it; the South American government and everyone else thought it was an excellent idea. All kinds of people became involved, from the President down to the provincial governor. All the people were excited, they had a big dedication ceremony, and installed two million dollars worth of barns, cattle, and all the rest. Then came the horrible confrontation that people did not like the taste of milk, and the whole enterprise failed. No one had thought to check that little factor beforehand.

The problem of educating people or converting tastes is an enormous one. I have been all over the world where people of goodwill have brought in sources of food which were nonconventional: food the people would not eat until someone was clever enough to disguise it, deoderize it, reoderize it, hide it in something else, or slowly and insidiously insert it, whereupon a taste was acquired. This is not done casually, it is not done easily, but I suggest that with the great persuasive powers we have to make people do and buy all kinds of things that they do not want to, this may not be beyond the scope of the United States in 1967.

As far as the kinds of things we can do because we have the knowledge, I think it is merely getting the appropriate disciplines, specialties, or whatever you wish to call them, together, and actually to go about solving some of these problems that are real, present, and upon us, not only here, but elsewhere in the world.

# HELLER

Much can be done about Indian starvation, but if you have ever been there, you have seen the illiterate and the essentially primitive people and the job it is, trying to get them to convert their agricultural methods. It is not an easy task, and just because you have a few solutions, it does not mean you are going to be able to sell them very readily, so the first job that we have is merely consolidating the knowledge and the gains already at hand, many of which Dr. Schaefer has consolidated in his brief talk.

I would like to give a little more time to some of the more esoteric items of the future.

The sea is obviously there and it is full of things, most of which we do not know anything about. When the pharmaceutical companies discovered molds, antibiotics coming from strange places, they began to take samples everywhere, from the arctic tundra to anybody's back yard. Some of the major firms had their plants literally on the sea, and the suggestions were made by many, "Why don't you look there?" They said, "We do not have anyone competent in marine biology." This is kind of a staggering stupidity when you see the tens of millions put into random research. Yet they did not have anybody competent to figure out how to grow marine organisms. Not that it is simple, not that you do not have to devise certain techniques, but that resources out there in terms of chemicals, hormones, all kinds of molecular structures that can be useful to man have not even been tapped or approached.

As an example of some of the strange possibilities

[51]

which may be inherent, some of us have had something to do with that finny friend of ours, the shark. This is a very primitive creature. Relatively speaking, he is unchanged in an evolutionary sense more or less for the last three hundred or three hundred fifty million years, which means he is enormously successful as he is. If you do not believe it, you should meet one under water some time and you will be rapidly convinced. This very primitive fish that does not yet have any bones, indicating how far he is back in the evolutionary scale, still is a remarkable source of materials. For instance, he has quite a few of the steroids that are in man, in your adrenal glands, the identical molecules. He has in the pituitary another molecule which is remarkably like that which is in man and which is lactogenic; it produces milk. When injected into a rabbit it is far more effective than the lactogenic hormone in the rabbit itself. Here is a fish, not a mammal; a three hundred fifty million year old fish that existed long before mammals even came on the surface of the earth, and it seems to suggest that when nature finds a very useful molecule it holds on to it not only though species but through evolution, through millennia and through hundreds of millennia.

Recently some of us have been taking a look at a peculiar material, a lipid, which is in the species of certain sharks and which seems to stimulate resistance in mammals. This is one of the strange things that laymen, doctors and other people have talked about, people's resistance being good or poor. It is well known that when you go out into strange places, strange for the people you are sending there, whether it be Southeast Asia or elsewhere, a large number are going to be ill. It is quite well known that there is always a small number of people who seem to be singularly immune. They drink the same water, are bitten by the same mosquitoes, and never seem to get anything. Whatever it is, it seems like a great idea to find out what the resistance factor is, and maybe bottle it. It looks as though such a material may be derived from the liver of certain sharks to stimulate the resistance of mammals against a variety of diseases.

I have come in contact with people in a major government agency involved with fish-flour, and some of them are very frightened of a thing called fish poison. This is a material which is picked up by virtually all predatory fish. Presumably it comes from low in the food chain, deposits in the fish muscle. It does not bother the fish, but it does affect man. Anyone who has been down in the Caribbean for a long time knows about it, and has probably had this type of fish poisoning. The statistics are very poor on it because people normally stay at home as they do with the measles, and only the bad cases finally go to the hospital so that everyone hears about it. There are some people who are rather worried about this because if this poison ever got into the fish protein and was not taken out, and we sent it abroad as a goodwill gesture, and we lost a few thousand, this could be rather awkward. They do not know how to try to isolate this chemically

[53]

and to identify it. This is fantastic, and yet they are putting a lot of money into it.

Another agency was extremely anxious and worried about shellfish toxin which is one of the most toxic materials known. One area of the government had apparently, I am told, cracked the chemical structure, but it was so classified that no one else could be told, so they would have to begin all over again. They were beginning with chemical methods which I suggest are about thirty to forty years old, as opposed to some of the new ones which could probably solve the problem for them in something like a year, instead of what would normally take thirty to forty years. What I am trying to point out is that there is a tremendous need for an interdisciplinary approach to the various problems that we have, because things do not exist in a vacuum, but in a universe. As a matter of fact, the universe, the natural world around us, is a continuum, and attempts to fragment it do violence to the whole. Man has fragmented it. This has been an institutional convenience. We need specialists, but we also need people who can go across disciplines and through disciplinary boundaries. Several recent reports from some of my colleagues have particular significance.

There is a new molecule which can be synthesized, which looks as though it can work in the sea, below the surface, in flat plaques, converting solar energy into electricity at possibly seventy percent efficiency compared to the current solar cells, which are used on space vehicles, and which have about ten percent efficiency. The new molecule can stand a reasonably

[54]

theoretical chance of being used on the continental shelf. Another molecule is available which can selectively take up such esoteric atoms as uropeum or scandium singularly from the sea and none other.

There is a great variety of extremely exciting potentials that offer opportunities from disciplines which currently exist. The sea is part of nature; it is a place where an interdisciplinary approach is not only needed, but one which quite literally commands such an approach.

### QUESTIONS

*Question:* We always worry about over harvesting the sea, and we are doing a good job of killing our fish with all the hydrocarbons we are pouring in there. In this country we have a high percentage of DDT in the seas. How much has been done to protect the public, and how much are we here going to do about it if you think it is as important as it seems to be in your book? Not only the life of the fish, but the lives of humans are being highly endangered.

*Dr. Heller:* The trouble with writing a book is that it is obsolete the minute you put down the last period. I am going to answer this question in a very different way. I think one of the problems with science is that, with our excess of competency in many areas and our rather tunnel vision aspect of looking at many problems, we suggest that someone find something which will kill this bug, and they will, and they have, and it is enormously successful. What it does to the rest of the ecological system is not normally seen until the damage has been done. I suggest a couple of other things, not looking backwards but looking ahead. There is something novel and potentially available which may reverse the host-parasite equilibrium in favor of the host. It will save lives primarily in the underdeveloped countries where there is today gross overpopulation. Will we be doing these people favors by saving their lives only to have them die of starvation at the age of five or six years? We have many powerful strengths; we take a unitary approach to solve a problem without thinking the thing through to the end. A little better planning in advance is extremely necessary if we are going to save ourselves from rather grievous damage.

*Question:* When the fact was mentioned that a number of programs need a low source of power, do any of these programs take into consideration the utilization of the sea to provide power?

*Dr. Heller:* Tidal engineers and tidal engineering have proved a fashionable and theoretical subject for quite some time. People have worked in tidal engineering; mock-up models have been planned. They have actually made small prototypes, but I know very little of any program that is being funded.

In terms of energy that is essentially cosmic in nature or celestial, or in other words, the tides, the moon, the sun, etc., if they are going to provide these as sources of energy they will be relatively cheap sources, provided, of course, they can be harnessed cheaply.

V

# CONDENSATION OF ATMOSPHERIC MOISTURE FROM TROPICAL MARITIME AIR MASSES AS A FRESHWATER RESOURCE

Robert D. Gerard, M.Sc.

*Research Associate, Lamont Geological Observatory, Columbia University*

It is a pleasure to participate in the conference and dedication of this laboratory and to welcome on behalf of Columbia University and the Lamont Observatory this new laboratory among the oceanographic fraternity. I am sure that the goals of excellence that are represented by Fairleigh Dickinson will be pursued with vigor in this new enterprise. Columbia is one of the oldest universities, while Fairleigh Dickinson is certainly among the younger and more vigorous institutions of higher education in our country. Columbia was already well under way in the 1770's, when Alexander Hamilton left his desk in Christiansted in St. Croix and went there as an undergraduate. Our oceanographic laboratory, however, is only eighteen years old. This would seem quite recent, but we must remember that eighteen years ago there were in the United States only about a half dozen private institutions in oceanography. Therefore, we are in fact an old-timer in oceanography, and as such perhaps we can be forgiven a bit of patronizing if we offer some advice to this new promising enterprise at St. Croix.

[57]

# CONDENSATION OF ATMOSPHERIC MOISTURE

One piece of advice might be that while pursuing the ideal of excellence in the various disciplines of marine biology, we recognize that physical oceanography is a broadly based oceanographic program which we presume will be followed here as time goes along; that the direction of this institution should not neglect the element of practicality in devoting some of its purely scientific and academic efforts towards the solution of problems important to society. I would like to present a scheme that in a way represents a focus of oceanographic disciplines upon one such problem.

Dr. Worzel, associate director at Lamont, and I have recently put together a combination of oceanographic disciplines towards the solution of a problem that appears to be quite an important one in an area such as this. Before making this presentation, I would like to make a couple of modifying statements, so that I shall not leave the wrong impression. First of all, this scheme is devoted to recovering water in a practical and very economical way in quantities that would be considered a water resource for an island or coastal area. This is not, nor does it pretend to be, an overall solution that will satisfy all problems. It may not even work, but it appears to be worth a study. Secondly, let me say that I am no expert in water resources, nor is Dr. Worzel, and we are the first to admit it.

In outlining this scheme, it should be kept in mind that it is not specific as a recommendation for this new laboratory, nor is it specific for St. Croix, but it might work out very well in this area. All of the Caribbean islands situated in the trade winds belt have a water resource of inestimable quantity. We judge that something like three hundred million gallons of water per day sweep across every mile of shoreline exposed to the tradewinds, and this is considering only the moisture contained in the bottom three hundred feet of the atmosphere. This is an enormous resource. We think it is possible to tap a small quantity of this, using the following elements of nature to our advantage: First of all, we require a coastal location; secondly, our location must be in the regular path of the trade winds; and thirdly, we need offshore ocean depth that brings cold water within close reach of the shoreline. With those three elements we can put together a recovery system as follows: We may pump the deep cold offshore water to condensers set up in the path of the trade winds. The winds will condense a considerable portion of their moisture passing through these large condensers, and this water may be recovered and used as potable water. There are some side benefits derived from this. One is that the water that we bring up from depth is from the richest nutrient level. At about a thousand meters depth off the shores of the Virgin Islands and in fact throughout the tropical ocean area we find the richest nutrient layers of the ocean. Here the nutrient salts, phosphates and nitrates, are ten to twenty times the concentration that you find in surface waters.

Many suggestions have been made as to ways to bring up this nutrient-rich water to fertilize the surface layers. Gifford Pinchot Jr. recently made a recommendation for utilizing the nutrient-rich layers to be pumped up and put to use in certain atolls within which one might raise whales. This scheme has been called the "Coral Corral." Dr. Schaefer also indicated that, if you can bring up these nutrient-rich waters and use them in restricted areas, you could have an enriched aquaculture or fish farming situation.

Let us look at some of these features one by one. The trade winds cover perhaps thirty-one percent of the ocean surface. These are the areas between ten and twenty degrees north and south of the equator. The winds here have the reputation of being the most reliable constant wind systems anywhere. They have, in addition, the characteristics of what the climatologists call maritime tropical air masses. They constantly have a high humidity. While not noticeably deficient in rainfall, the islands in these areas frequently suffer from water shortage. The Virgin Islands are no exception. We know the large islands in the Caribbean, such as Puerto Rico, Jamaica and Martinique, have local influence on the climate due to their larger area and higher mountains. Smaller islands, however, do not have the size or elevation that causes local conditions favorable to rainfall. In fact, although the rainfall here is approximately the same as in New York, the high evaporation rate and certain ground water problems compound the difficulty and make it a water-short area, as we are well aware.

Let us examine the typical installation that we might set up in St. Croix using these cold offshore waters. St. Croix is surrounded by deep water. Within a mile in nearly any direction from the shore, you can reach water that is two or three thousand feet deep. The water here has a temperature of about four or five degrees centigrade. This is roughly forty degrees fahrenheit, the temperature of your refrigerator. We therefore have two of the elements that we need to bring about this water condensation scheme: the cold offshore water and the trade winds with their constancy and their high humidity.

Let us consider how to set up a plant producing one million gallons of fresh water per day and utilizing these natural advantages. We require an underwater pipe, about three feet in diameter and about a mile long, if we choose the right spot in St. Croix proximate to deep water. Through this pipe we will draw up cold water to our condenser. A few calculations tell us that, if we reduce the temperature of the air from about seventy-five degrees to about fifty-five degrees, we can recover approximately twenty grams of water per cubic meter. This is a fair recovery; we are aware of it every time we have a cold scotch and soda and see the moisture condensing on the outside of the glass and perhaps making a small pool on the table. This is the kind of water that we are going to recover with our system. We will have to pump about thirty gallons of cold sea water to recover one gallon of fresh water. This means for our one million gallons a day we will need to pump approximately thirty million gallons of salt water. This is not an imposing problem. There are pumps today that are highly efficient in handling quan-

# CONDENSATION OF ATMOSPHERIC MOISTURE

tities of this sort. The power required for such a pump is calculated to be about two hundred fifty horsepower. How do we get the power?

If we consider the constant winds of this area and observe the remains of numerous windmills, we are reminded that wind power has been used extensively in these islands. Dutch windmills of the sixteenth century were remarkable machines capable of pumping two thousand cubic feet of water per minute to a height of six feet. They developed about one hundred horsepower in a strong wind. A modern version of a windmill could be a very efficient system to recover power from the wind to produce electric power for pumping in our proposed water recovery system. Of course, careful projections of power cost, considering diesel generators and other sources, would have to be made for any proposed locality. Considering the small power cost and simple nature of our system, we believe it would produce potable water more cheaply than existing systems of the one million gallon per day scale.

The desalination plants that are being set up, for instance, in St. Thomas where the water problem is indeed very serious are, I believe, producing water for somewhat less than a dollar per thousand gallons. There have not been any detailed estimates of costs for our system and such estimates will have to wait the results of pilot studies before one can come to a realistic figure.

Let us look now at the general scheme that we have discussed. We have a long pipe extending out to the level of about a thousand meters depth offshore. Water comes to our pump set up at sea level and, using power perhaps generated by the wind, is pumped up to our condenser. The size of this condenser is another figure rather hard to calculate. It might possibly be a size of six hundred feet by about thirty feet high. This is a large structure but with appropriate design might even be an attractive one. Our condenser, set on a hilltop, intercepts the trade winds, condensing water, which flows to a storage area. Fortunately we do not have to turn this condenser to follow the wind because of the fact that the tradewinds come from the same quarter at all seasons of the year. There are problems, such as how to contend with salt crystals that are carried in the atmosphere, that may be very serious and have to be looked at. There are many questions as to how best to use the nutrient-rich water we will pump back into a lagoon for agriculture and biological experiments.

There is one more possible benefit from this system. We could develop a kind of local air-conditioning system using cool dehumidified air that comes from the condenser.

We have presented a scheme that focuses many facets of oceanographic discipline upon a problem in this area which is important to society and man's welfare.

### QUESTIONS

*Question:* How big is the diameter of the pipe? Have you figures on that?

# CONDENSATION OF ATMOSPHERIC MOISTURE

*Mr. Gerard:* In our sample one-million-gallon-per-day plant the pipe calculations were based on a three-foot diameter pipe. If this pipe were steel or iron, and therefore a good conductor of heat, it would have to be insulated in the upper several hundred meters at least. Here we run through the strongest gradient of temperature and we would want to prevent too much heat exchange in order to keep the water cold, so that we could use this as a cold source at the surface.

*Question:* Do you conceive of this plant being on the ground or is it possible, let us say, to have it out on a barge in the ocean?

*Mr. Gerard:* It brings up an interesting possibility. We actually have considered setting up such a plant on a ship. We know that at the time of the Cuban crisis a great effort was made to bring desalination plants from California to be set up at Guantanamo. There are many emergencies, earthquakes and national disasters as well, that jeopardize water systems in coastal cities. It is quite possible to set up such a system as a portable or a moving kind of system on a ship. A tanker, for instance, would have the area for exposure to the wind if it had this large condenser set up as a super-structure, and would have the water storage capability, and could lay offshore in water of sufficient depth to drop down its pumps and begin to use this system. I think it is perfectly possible to do it from a floating platform.

# GERARD

*Question:* I was wondering if you mentioned whether the water going into the lagoon was water that was condensed or water that was pumped up?

*Mr. Gerard:* This is the pure sea water, but differing from normal surface sea water in that it is highly enriched with phosphates and nitrates.

*Question:* What do you do with the water that is condensed?

*Mr. Gerard:* Collect it in a reservoir, hopefully a covered one because of the high evaporation in these parts.

*Question:* I am sure that you must have considered atomic power. What has been your experience?

*Mr. Gerard:* We understand that there is a great deal of development going on to have combination atomic power and desalination plants. These dual purpose plants supposedly will give us water for under fifty cents per thousand gallons. In these plants efficiency is related to scale, the larger the better.

*Question:* Has not commercial production of water been brought down to twenty-five cents a thousand gallons?

*Mr. Gerard:* The figures are hard to analyze. Sometimes they do not include capital costs; sometimes they show only operating costs. I think the best answer to these economic problems in this area would be to check with St. Thomas where they have two one-million-gallon-a-day plants operating at the present time.

[65]

# CONDENSATION OF ATMOSPHERIC MOISTURE

*Question:* Who operates them?

*Mr. Gerard:* I do not know; presumably the Virgin Islands government, the Public Works Department.

*Question:* What are the capital costs of such a plant? The whole question here is probably an economic one. Can you make it cheaper your way than by desalination?

*Mr. Gerard:* I think so on the scale we have discussed. It appears that our system has a low operating cost. The capital costs are extremely difficult to examine. I know of no one who has made a condenser of this size, but I think that no matter how you look at it, it could hardly cost more than the systems now being used. There is a great deal of technology developing with regard to the most efficient surfaces for condensers. For instance, polished gold is about the most perfect surface for a condenser; it induces condensation allowing the heat conductivity to go ahead at its most efficient rate, removing the water, and preventing an insulating film of water from collecting. Condensers of large size are becoming more and more practical.

*Question:* Has anyone approximated the salvage value of the minerals, not only the phosphates and nitrates and fertilizers, but some of the rare elements which we sorely need and do not know where to find?

*Mr. Gerard:* I think that it is not the kind of system that would lend itself to economic recovery of dissolved materials in the water. In desalination you have already made a concentrate of these dissolved materials that could lead you to recover selected ones among them. We are not processing the sea water in any way in this scheme. We are simply taking it up, using it for its cold property, and putting it back into the sea. You would have to set up an additional stage for the recovery of any dissolved minerals. Desalination is quite economical in the Gulf Coast, for example, where magnesium is taken out of the sea commercially.

# VI

## OCEAN ENGINEERING

### Willard Bascom

*President and Chairman, Ocean Science and Engineering, Inc.*

I offer congratulations to Fairleigh Dickinson for having begun the establishment of a marine biology laboratory here. I have been asked to talk about ocean engineering and I shall do so in rather broad terms. I suppose the first question is "What is ocean engineering and what do ocean engineers do?" The general task of an engineer is to design and build equipment of value to mankind. If you want a job done fast, inexpensively, and right, you hire an engineer to do it. I keep thinking that science today is sort of a tiny flower growing on top of a tremendous pyramid of engineering. Engineers furnish the frameworks and supporting structure—and are also concerned with finance and economics more than scientists.

What is ocean engineering? Let us think first about any profession that is involved with the ocean. The ocean is simply a place to work. When people who are already biologists, physicists, or chemists go to work in the ocean, we call them marine biologists, marine physicists, or marine chemists. The same is true of engineers who are simply men trained to carry out their profession in the ocean. The difference is, of course, the nature of the ocean itself, so that there is a tremendous accent these days on the understanding of the ocean environment as it influences the professions.

For example, no one can really go to sea without a ship. A ship means that someone somewhere has to design it, model test it in a tank, finance it, get it built in a shipyard, review the construction, test it at sea, and deliver it somewhere so that it can do a specific job for a specific length of time, etc. The ship has to use harbors, and the harbors have to be designed and dredged. Breakwaters, jetties and piers all have to be designed by engineers. To the oil industry ocean engineering means the design of drilling platforms and floating rigs, undersea wellheads, pipes to carry the oil ashore, etc. All of these things must operate under unusual and difficult conditions which range from a flat calm over most of the year, to a violent hurricane for two or three days a year.

You can imagine many more engineering problems. I think it will be more to the point if I treat specifically what our company is doing because, first of all, that is an area in which I can claim some competence. Secondly, the examples I can offer may give you a more realistic idea of ocean engineering in the world today. Our company is a new one, only five years old, but in that length of time we have spread around the earth. We have six subsidiaries working in about a dozen countries; five ships at sea; and a professional staff with broad experience. The reason we have gone so far afield is not exactly through choice (because it obviously makes for difficult management) but because there is no concentration of business in any one area. We must go find it if we want it, so we do a little

[69]

bit of business everywhere. I can start by telling you about our adventures with ships.

We now have a fleet of about five ships, and there are several more on the drawing boards. We will be building more ships. Our latest ship is now undergoing radical modification in our yards at West Palm Beach, Florida. It is a 220-foot vessel, cruises at fourteen knots, and can spend forty-five days at sea with a crew of forty-five people on it. It will probably be the most modern oil geophysical ship in the world. It will have deep seismic gear on it for probing the rocks beneath the sea to depths of fifteen to twenty thousand feet. There will also be continuously operating gravitymeters, magnetometers, and several very fancy navigation systems—the one in use depending to some extent on the area of the world in which the ship is operating. The complete cost of that ship will be about 1.5 million dollars, and the first problem is where to raise the money to buy it. One always comes back to money. The previous ship built was the Oceaneer, a much smaller vessel built for deep sea research, which we designed and had built from the keel up. It is operating at the moment for the University of Washington's deep sea research project on the northwest Pacific coast of the United States. Oceaneer is one hundred feet long, has deep sea winches, radar, echo-sounders, loran navigation, etc. Another vessel has recently returned from about a year's prospecting for tin off the coast of Australia. It has just come back to our Pacific coast base and is now out installing

BASCOM

some fancy buoys for the Coast and Geodetic Survey.
Two other vessels are in Viet Nam, where they serve
as housekeeping and survey ships for several survey
parties we have in the rivers and harbors of the forward area.

Besides this we design and have ships built on contract for other people. We have designed small submarines and submarine tenders, some unusual drilling
ships and a family of work ships.

We also do several kinds of surveying. For example, we survey for pipeline and cable routes using unusual geophysical methods. We do sand surveys and
beach inventories to discover where the supply of
offshore sand is. Then we design ways of pumping it
ashore to use for beach nourishment. Surveys like
this were made for Florida, California, Hawaii and
several other places in the world. We do harbor-type
surveys, one of which was a survey of Cape Town
Harbor in South Africa to determine the location of
channels, piers, etc.

The most interesting survey that we have made is
one in which we explored for diamonds along the coast
of South and Southwest Africa. About four years ago
we signed a contract with the De Beers Corporation
to prospect four major diamond concessions along
the African coast. As part of that work we built several
most unusual sampling and prospecting ships. You
may be interested to know how that came about. In
1961 De Beers was operating a diamond mine on the
coast of Southwest Africa close to the mouth of the
Orange River. It is the largest mine in the world, ex-

[71]

tending along the coast for over one hundred kilometers, and probably the most profitable. They admit to a one hundred percent profit per year. It is a very good mine indeed, and as the mine has grown larger their power requirements have increased considerably until they decided that it would be more efficient if they could convert from trucking fuel for their large diesel power plant to a pipeline out to sea where tankers would pump the fuel ashore. This is a customary procedure. However, their coast and the waves that break on it are unusually rough and the situation is difficult. They invited a series of pipeline contractors to come and inspect the property and bid on what they would do. As it turned out, one of the contractors who came was an unusual fellow who managed immediately to alienate the mine manager—but before he left he suggested that the De Beers Company should mine the diamonds that were just offshore. Having been in the diamond business a long time, they answered that there were not many diamonds offshore, and if there were they could not be mined. The contractor decided to try for himself, and so got a ship, took up a concession from the government of Southwest Africa, and started looking. He eventually found a few diamonds and came back to the De Beers company and said, "Are you sure you wouldn't like to go into the undersea diamond business with me?"

De Beers declined. The diamond business is very complicated and not suitable for amateurs at all, particularly when it involves the grading and evaluation of diamonds, cutting them, selling them, etc. But since the De Beers company said they did not want to be involved, our determined contractor raised some money, built a diamond dredge, and started bringing up diamonds from the sea floor. On some days he would get as much as a thousand carats. After this went on for awhile, the suspicion grew in the minds of the De Beers' management that maybe there really were diamonds under the sea. By this time, of course, they were in a very bad bargaining position. At that time I walked in and asked why they did not let our company serve as arbiter to determine the extent and value of the deposits, whatever they might be. Since both sides were trying to get out of the difficult situation, they agreed that that was a good idea, so they engaged Ocean Science and Engineering to conduct some extensive surveys to determine the extent, quality and character of the diamond deposits.

We began by making a rather elaborate geophysical survey, eventually covering over six hundred miles of the coast of southern Africa, and we followed it up with an extensive sampling program for which we built the special drilling ship Rockeater. We stayed for about two and one-half years in Southwest Africa, completing this contract. In the end we presented De Beers with a very large map showing little red areas marked with the areas that have diamonds, with so many carats per square meter, etc.

Certain difficulties developed within the country and it was decided that our company should not be involved in the actual mining operations. But, together with the De Beers company, we formed the

# OCEAN ENGINEERING

Ocean Mining A.G. of Zug, Switzerland, and with that company we set about exploring the rest of the world's oceans for other kinds of minerals. That was about three years ago, and we now own rather extensive concessions (and applications which will probably be granted) in Australia, Central America, Alaska, Tasmania, Thailand, Malaya, Indonesia, the Philippines, etc. We have men out all the time looking for other prospects.

Usually the terms of concessions are such that when a company is given a concession by a government, it must then guarantee to spend so much money in surveying and prospecting the concession. We have finished doing this in about three or four places now. We usually agree to turn over all our survey data and some of our samples to the government so that they can make their own appraisal of it. This has been a very satisfactory arrangement.

However, the job is only one-quarter done the day when the prospecting is completed, the geological results are analyzed, and we can say, for example, "Here is an area of so many square miles that contains so many dollars per cubic meter of tin." That is only the beginning of an undersea mining project. Many people think that if you have found an ore deposit you are as good as rich. Not quite! Now you must begin a difficult and detailed economic analysis which may require you to design three or four kinds of dredges, several metallurgical methods, operating systems, sales programs, etc. This becomes a vast chart which you use to play games with a computer to determine how to make the maximum amount of money. This is a long and arduous task. Yet after having made these studies and having determined the best plan, it must still be made into a business proposal which will then be discussed with your major corporate partners and your bank. Undersea mining is a very complicated business, and finding the ore is only one small part of it. But we are willing to accept the difficulties and we have men and ships working overseas in several countries making the necessary studies.

Our company is also involved in engineering design of all sorts of oceanic hardware. We have built many different kinds of special winches and instruments. We do a lot of design contracting and construction of unusual components, specializing mainly in hardware design for unique ocean projects. Often the unique aspect which we concentrate on has to do with dynamic or moving stresses. That is to say, a winch that may be perfectly fine for use as a mine hoist, for example, where one is dealing with the same gravitational forces all the time, would not be satisfactory on shipboard because of the unusual motions and accelerations of a ship. It may have to be redesigned completely. Then too, at sea there are all the usual problems of corrosion, electrolysis, fatigue, power supply, etc.

In the long run OSE/E intends to be a resources company. Contracting is merely a mechanism for getting us into business and building up a staff. We are not at all pleased with the prospect of spending the rest of our lives writing proposals to governments,

[75]

# OCEAN ENGINEERING

or to other companies, about what we will do for them. We intend to work for ourselves.

Already we are betting rather large sums of money on our own ability to find and develop mineral, fishery, and petroleum resources from the sea. Today, although there are a lot of people talking about the vast resources of the sea, there are very few who are backing up their talk with hard work and cash. Our group has left the talking stage behind; we are now developing the ocean's resources.

### QUESTIONS

*Question:* With your vast knowledge of engineering of the ocean, would your company undertake the project such as outlined by Mr. Gerard, and if so, how long would it take to execute it?

*Mr. Bascom:* We have often said we will undertake anything in the ocean anywhere. It is a sort of a gambit. It is, of course, only partially true. There are certain things which are not within our competence, but what Mr. Gerard has been talking about is precisely what we do, unusual engineering jobs in the ocean. As a matter of fact, when I listened to him I had two thoughts which I suppose he shared but did not mention. One is, I guess in the beginning this project will be located on top of a hill. This makes it easy to deliver the water to the place you want it. With most systems proposed you get the fresh water at the beach edge and you have to pump it uphill to use it, but with this scheme you have some water up there at the place you need it. Secondly, it would be quite an expense to conduct this experiment.

Now, as to what OSE/E would do, we are in the business of designing and laying out pipelines and figuring out exactly how big they should be and what the thermodynamics of the problem are. So Mr. Gerard's project is very much in our area; in my judgment, it is probably possible to make a cost estimate. Basically I would agree with Mr. Gerard that this system should be investigated. After investigating it, someone should look at it *relative* to other things you can do to get water. One must make a systems analysis, and then the best system wins, or should win, unless you have some overriding reason for not following the answer you come up with.

*Question:* I would like to ask Mr. Bascom what the overall budget in the commercial sector is per year; that is, what do you estimate a company like yours and certain other companies (perhaps oil companies) would have as an overall budget in relation to the exploration in the commercial section?

*Mr. Bascom:* I really have not the faintest idea what it is. You see, the one characteristic that engineers have, which is usually different from scientists, is that they deal with realities instead of abstractions. If you have a problem that you would like me to solve, I can perhaps solve it for you, but if you ask me generalities like what everyone else in the world is doing or should do, I have not the faintest idea. Consequently, I am always hopelessly inadequate in judging what the government should do, or what someone's budget should be. I do not know how you answer questions like these. I have just come from a three-day long-range planning conference our company held in Mexico, where we all talked about what our grand goals and objectives are. We picked out five major areas and decided to concentrate everything in them and to throw away jobs that do not fall into those areas.

*Question:* How about solar power? Have you considered that?
*Mr. Bascom:* No.

*Question:* Our students at the University of New York often ask us what the job opportunities are going to be in the ocean area, and specifically what sort of people do you expect when you hire them?
*Mr. Bascom:* The question has to do with job opportunities in the ocean. We are primarily an engineering firm. The scientists in our company are primarily electronics people, or they are geologists doing new things in a new way, but it is not what I would really call highpowered science. Mostly we use naval architects, mechanical engineers, electrical and electronic engineers, mining engineers and that sort of people. In order to sell your students to our market, you must offer us engineers who are trained along these lines, and they presumably will have done some graduate work in the oceanic environment. We have no use for skin divers or for people who claim to have spent time around yachts, and would now like to go to work for a

living. We deal with highly trained professional people.

*Question:* How many persons do you have in your organization?
*Mr. Bascom:* I am asked this question very often and I am not sure what the answer is. If we only count senior professional engineers and geologists, usually with a master's degree or better, we have about forty-five of them.

*Question:* I understand that you have to guarantee a government a certain amount of money. In other words, after you finish your survey, what rights do you keep?
*Mr. Bascom:* This is a complicated question; it has to do with rights and concessions. The answer is that every country is different and usually every state in every country is different. Our most recent large survey was for the State of Tasmania, one of the states of Australia, and there we have an exclusive arrangement. We would not consider surveying any area where we would not have exclusive and continuing rights. In most countries the wording is different but what it amounts to is an exclusive prospecting license which is convertible to a mine or lease under certain terms and conditions which usually are specified in advance. In Tasmania last year we spent about $750,000 on our surveys, which is an appreciable amount of money to raise when you are a long way from having returns. Every country is a little bit different. In

[79]

Thailand we had to make application in each state individually, for something like four acres at a time. In Malaysia, somewhat to our horror, they were trying to give us a whole continental shelf, and you must remember that Malaysia includes Borneo and it is a long way from Malaysia to Borneo. In Indonesia we are still dickering. There are complications there which have to do with military operations still going on in certain parts of the islands, and certain areas are being reserved for unexplained reasons. In every case we will end up with exclusive rights that are convertible to leases under some sort of terms, and in many of these emerging countries such as Indonesia, it is illegal for them to give away land or concessions. In effect, a company is formed in which you are in partnership with the government. The outside interests put up all the capital costs. By the way, in most cases those costs are considerable, because a minimum mining dredge costs five million dollars and up. The country allows you to write off capital expenses at an agreed amortization rate and to take operating costs from the first returns; beyond that we will split the profit fifty-fifty with the government. The government's fifty percent includes everything it gets whether it be called taxes, or royalties, or anything else. In most of these arrangements there are very complicated agreements about foreign exchange, and where the material is to be smelted, and how it will be processed and sold, and many other things which are too complicated to go into.

*Question:* Are there any working arrangements with schools to provide training?

*Mr. Bascom:* Mr. Abel is of course very much involved in helping to finance schools which are interested in sea grant programs, and we are establishing some in several places. I hope that before long, for example, we will have one in Florida.

*Question:* What is happening now in oceanography is really what happened with the schools of mining in the nineteenth century. When mining became important, the schools developed as the need for mining engineering became apparent. Now we have a broad new area, and it seems to me that Fairleigh Dickinson University would be in an ideal position to have the kind of curriculum and the kind of syllabi within the curriculum that would make sense in the terms of the needs of today. Do you think so?

*Mr. Bascom:* Mining is about as special as oceanography, so you are simply compounding the problem. What we are really asking for are just basic engineers. It is not too important which area they were trained in, just so they fundamentally understand engineering. The details of either mining or oceanography are something that industry can fairly easily teach. In fact, they would probably be better trained by the group that they are going to work with, so if you are going to be in this business what you really want to turn out is first-class engineers and then give them some graduate work in either of these two areas— mining or oceanography.

[81]

*Question:* Do you not need to have an added element, a willingness, a slant, or desire on the part of the student who enters this area of work?

*Mr. Bascom:* There is no doubt that you are always better off with self-motivated people, and I should add that we do not even hire anyone that has not been to sea before. We want people with some sea-going experience, simply because it is almost impossible to explain the ocean to somebody who has not been to sea in at least one big storm. That is very important. I did not mean to be answering for industry as a whole. You asked what we could use now. We could use engineers; someone else may have a need for men with other requirements.

*Question:* What about the family life of these men? What happens? Are most of these young scientists people who have no family, or do they just leave their family behind for an appreciable part of the year?

*Mr. Bascom:* Generally, you cannot send families along with the survey crews. First of all, the crews are always on the move, so there is no one place you could send a family. We have moved families to parts of South Africa and Australia which are remote from the United States. They are as pleasant as the United States, only different. We send ships to sea, but we do give the crews satisfactory compensatory time off and they get maybe a month's vacation each year.

*Comment by Mr. Gerard:* At Lamont we run an operation that is somewhat unique among the oceanographic institutions. Our ships go out frequently for eleven months of the year. This means that they are away from the home port for very nearly a full year. They touch into various ports around the world about every thirty or forty days, but it does not offer any opportunities for meeting one's family unless one has a very transient sort of family to deal with. Some go out for segments of these long cruises, but we try wherever possible to have sustaining people for an entire cruise; we try to keep the continuity among the technicians and the scientific aides on shipboard.

*Mr. Bascom:* On this same point, there is something I would like to comment on. Periodically somebody says, "How is the United States doing relative to Russia?" Generally, I have not the faintest idea what the answer is to that question. My observation of Russian ships (I have been on three of them) is that they have one big advantage over the United States. They send their scientists to sea and the scientists stay at sea for a year at a time. Our scientists, on the other hand, are rarely willing to be gone more than a month or two, and then they must be flown out to meet a ship overseas.

# VII

# INTERNATIONAL ASPECTS OF OCEANOGRAPHY

## Arthur E. Maxwell, Ph.D.

*Associate Director, Woods Hole Oceanographic Institution*

I shall discuss some of the international implications of oceanography; some changes that have taken place in the last few years, some of the problems that have arisen, and perhaps even suggest some solutions. Before I get into this, I would like to present some background about the importance of these oceans for the world as a whole. We have had much background already on this from the previous speakers and a good deal more has been written about it. As Mr. Bascom mentioned, I think that to most of us who are in the business, the noise is much louder than the signal here, and there is a lot more talk than action. Nevertheless, I think, even assuming the most conservative attitude, it is difficult to conclude other than that man is going to return to the sea in the near future for many of his needs.

This conclusion can be drawn from examining the technological and sociological revolution that is taking place around us—for example, we have seen computers developed to the point where thinking people are worried about thinking machines—the development of nuclear power has had an impact on the constraints and ramifications of the actions of nations. We see action in outer space that we would probably

[84]

have considered miraculous a few years ago; communications such as television have revised our lives completely, and in addition to this we hear of the so-called population explosion where it is estimated by experts that the population of the world will actually double within the next thirty to forty years. I think a combination of these tremendous demands for resources to meet the accelerating needs of this technological and human revolution, plus man's natural inclination to turn to the unknown—the sea—is going to provide the impetus for him going into the ocean.

As we have seen, a large step has already taken place. It is really only a sense of urgency that is lacking, and in some instances this urgency has been provided: for example, by the loss of the Thresher in 1963; by the loss of the H-bomb off Palomares last year, and most recently by the sinking of the supertanker Torrey Canyon in England. None of these events has had the dramatic impact of Sputnik, but certainly all of them are beginning to focus our attention on the importance of the ocean, particularly the international importance, and its potential influence on national politics. It is this last point that I would like to discuss a little more in detail.

If we develop an understanding of the oceans and the technological capability to reap its benefits, it is equally important that we develop the sociological attitude to use these resources for the maximum benefit of mankind. We must continue to be a master of our sea technology rather than let it become a master of us. There is a danger that a few ocean-oriented powers,

[85]

because of their superior technical capabilities, will appropriate the vast riches of the ocean and use them for their own well-being. I think President Johnson in his dedication of the Oceanographer a year or so ago expressed this concern quite succinctly, and I quote him, "Under no circumstances, we believe, must we ever allow the prospects of rich harvests and mineral wealth to create a new form of colonial competition among the maritime nations. We must be careful to avoid a race to grab and hold the lands under the high seas. We must ensure that the deep seas and the ocean bottoms are and remain the legacy of all human beings."

In essence we find ourselves on the threshold of a major embarkation into space and sea exploration and exploitation, and the time has arrived when we must consider the implications involved. Some hard thought therefore has to be given to what legally might be called the public order of the sea.

As further background I would like to review the status of the present regime or system of laws that govern the research, exploration and exploitation of the high seas. It is not surprising perhaps to realize that these have evolved from essentially zero in 1945 to what exist today. In 1945, President Truman initiated a national order by two proclamations. The first of these extended the jurisdiction of the United States to include the resources of the continental shelf adjacent to its coast and the result was the establishment of fishing zones in the high seas off its coasts to aid in the conservation of these resources. This action was followed by considerable litigation in the courts, principally between the states and the federal government, over the right to collect the oil royalties from these areas. The court action was resolved by the Outer Continental Shelf Act of 1950. From 1950 to 1956 the International Law Commission evolved a series of conventions that were adopted at a Conference on the Law of the Seas convened by the United Nations at Geneva in 1958. By 1964 all four conventions adopted at Geneva were ratified by the twenty-two nations required to bring them into force. It is interesting to note that of the 135 national states which exist in the world today, 109 of these border on the sea. Forty have enacted legislation dealing with the continental shelf and thirty-six of these at this time have ratified the Law of the Sea Convention.

Two primary problems were not able to be resolved at the 1958 Law of the Sea Conference. The first of these was to determine whether the width of territorial seas was to be three, six, twelve or two hundred miles. Another conference held in 1960 did not resolve this matter, nor is it yet resolved. The second unresolved problem was the jurisdiction of fisheries on the high seas.

A third problem that was settled, at least for the time being, was the width of the continental shelf.

This was resolved by purposely adopting at the 1958 convention some ambiguous language which defines the width of the outer continental shelf. Again

# INTERNATIONAL ASPECTS
# OF OCEANOGRAPHY

I would like to quote: "The seabed and subsoil of the submarine areas adjacent to the coast, but outside the areas of the territorial sea, to a depth of two hundred meters or, beyond that limit, to where the depth of the superadjacent waters admits the exploitation of the natural resources of the same areas." In effect, it clearly says that the state owns its shelf out to two hundred meters and as far beyond that as it can exploit. This was purposefully vague, and it is its vagueness that is causing many of the difficulties we face in international aspects of the oceans at this time.

Fortunately considerable interest has been aroused in the legal aspects of the high seas in the last few years. For example, the University of Rhode Island convened a Law of the Sea Institute in 1966 to discuss this problem, and they have another meeting scheduled for later this month on the same problem. In addition, the Mershon Social Science Program of the Carnegie Endowment for International Peace, along with Ohio State University, jointly sponsored a conference on the Security, Organization, and Use of the Ocean this past March. They have a second conference scheduled for October of this year. Recently, the American Bar Association convened a four-day meeting on the subject in Long Beach, in which some of the country's leading legal experts participated. Further, the National Council on Marine Resources and Engineering Development, of which the Vice-President of the United States is Chairman, has in recent weeks contracted out six separate studies on this, with the seventh study about to be initiated.

One might well surmise, with all this activity on problems concerned with the legal regime of the seas that ought to govern the exploitation and exploration of the world's oceans, the situation should be well in hand. However, I think it is safe to say only that many alternatives have been identified and that many complicated factors exist. Many of these are conflicting requirements for use in the same areas of the sea, and it is obvious that there is not going to be either an easy or an early solution to what regime will eventually govern the exploitation of the sea floor.

A number of possibilities have received considerable attention. I shall mention a few of these. One is the laissez-faire attitude, or just to let things go as they have been going in the past with no specific action. Another concept is merely the extension of regional treaties. For example, there are a number of fishery treaties existing throughout the world today; this concept would be to divide the world up into generalized regions and to deal specifically with each of these. The third is the extension of natural boundaries for either the jurisdiction or the sovereignty; that is, to extend each country's own boundaries out to essentially the center of the ocean or to where they might intersect with other countries' boundaries. Another of the ideas proposed is to divide the oceans among the major maritime powers of the world. Still another possibility is to confer the ownership to an international organization, such as the United Nations,

[89]

which might lease out the properties and use this income to finance its operations. There have been discussions suggesting separate regimes for the water and the resources of the water as compared with the resources on the sea floor, and also to separate military requirements from commerce requirements. Of all of these, I think the situation most likely is converging on two: the first is international ownership of the ocean, by giving it to an international group such as the United Nations, and the second, the so-called Flag-Nation Regime, which means that any country that gets there first to exploit that part of the world has the right to the minerals thereon. This is essentially an extension of mining laws to the sea.

I shall not dwell on the many pros and cons that have been discussed at the several meetings mentioned above, but I would like to illustrate that each of these has its complications as well as its appeals. The proponents of the United Nations ownership assert that this would provide a mechanism whereby all the nations of the world would share in the wealth of the sea, no matter which nations were to exploit it. These proponents also mention that this would resolve problems of annexation, dividing up the sea or using it for military bases. They propose that no military work or bases be allowed in the oceans. These proponents cite the analogies such as the treaties that have been written for outer space and Antarctica as examples of how the oceans might be handled. Conversely, the opponents of the international group use the same arguments against them. They say that neither the space nor Antarctica examples are really germane, because the potential economic and security aspects of the ocean are much more obvious than they are either in outer space or in the Antarctic. Also they consider it premature at this time to move in this direction until more is known about the ocean and what role it will play in the future of our nations.

In general, this same group prefers the Flag-Nation approach because it appears to be more realistic and because it looks as though it will be a method that will encourage large capital expenditures required along the lines that were mentioned by Mr. Bascom and others. They also concede that there is some danger in this, as there will be conflict or competition for the land or the development of monopolistic tendencies. We have seen in the past where the United States and France have set up large areas of the Pacific Ocean for nuclear testing, and where the Soviets have also set up large areas for some of their rocket testing. It is difficult to see how this might be avoided in the future.

One definite conclusion that appears to be emerging from these discussions is that some sort of timely action is necessary. This is true if we ever wish to adopt the International Regime of the Seas even at a later date. It is necessary that action be taken now so that various nations of the world do not appropriate all the "land out at sea" by gradual encroachment through the extension of limits of the continental shelf. Many examples of this encroachment can be cited.

[91]

# INTERNATIONAL ASPECTS
# OF OCEANOGRAPHY

Within the United States only recently land has been leased off the east coast out to the depths of some five thousand feet and some three hundred miles offshore. These represent an extension of our interpretation of the outer limits of the continental boundary, and if *we* interpret the law in this way there is nothing to prevent other nations from doing it in a similar fashion until we find the whole ocean appropriated in this manner. We are faced with a dilemma of taking action either too late after the historical rights have been determined, or too soon before all the facts are in.

I would like to mention also some of the considerable interaction between oceanographic research and some of the legal aspects I have just discussed. For example, the evolution of international programs in oceanography has taken place parallel with that of the legal aspects, both in time and in scale. The first major cooperative international effort in oceanography began with the International Geophysical Year, the IGY, which lasted for eighteen months in 1957 and 1958. This was the outgrowth of the concept of an International Polar Year started in 1882, which was to be repeated every fifty years to look at the geophysics in the polar regions. However, the pace of science has been so great that the interval has been cut down to twenty-five years and the area expanded to include the whole earth. The motivation for this international effort in oceanography was cooperative research on a worldwide basis, but its acceptance among the oceanographic community was largely one of economic

necessity. Support for oceanography had been fluctu-
ating wildly about this time and the program appeared to be a solution. However, oceanographers
were quick to see the advantage of international cooperation and very soon thereafter an International
Indian Ocean Expedition was organized. This effort
saw the real beginning of cooperative planning and
analysis of data, with some twenty-three countries
participating and with forty ships and one hundred
eighty cruises over the period 1959 to 1965.

It was during the same interval that a mechanism
was evolved to plan and coordinate international research on a continuing basis. This was the Intergovernmental Oceanographic Commission organized under
UNESCO in 1960. The Commission, very soon after its
inception, assumed the responsibility for the coordination of the Indian Ocean Expedition. In its formative
years the Commission spent most of its efforts developing international programs in oceanography and me-
chanisms for the exchange of data between the Soviets
and the United States.

However, during the past few years there has been
a noticeable change in the character of the Commission. A great deal of its time has been spent on problems of assistance to less developed nations, the
pollution of the oceans and legal aspects of the sea.
Until recently these matters were not taken up in
context with exploiting the resources of the sea, but
were restricted to problems that had risen in connection with research at sea. However, the General
Assembly of the United Nations adopted a resolution

in November, 1966, to survey the marine activities of
all its members and to propose a cooperative international program in both oceanographic research and
exploitation of the marine resources, as well as to
recommend an effective arrangement to manage the
program. The Commission, seeing that this might
jeopardize its existence, rapidly changed its emphasis
to include both research and exploitation. At the Commission's Bureau meeting in January, 1967, the
Soviets proposed that working groups be established
to prepare conventions that would apply to research
at sea and also for purposes of exploiting the ocean's
mineral resources. These are to be discussed at the
Commission's next meeting in October of this year.
Therefore, in a relatively short time, from 1957 to
1967, the oceanographers have arrived at a position
where they are actually considering a public order of
the sea quite independent from the efforts that have
been undertaken by the legal experts.

Earlier I noted that there is some concern about
the timeliness for developing a regime for the high
seas. In this connection two courses of action seem to
be receiving some attention. One is to proceed by
convening another Conference on the Law of the Sea,
which would probably take several years to prepare
and several more years to ratify into force. A second
course would be to gain experience through exploitation of the sea utilizing the Flag-Nation approach to
establish a set of historical precedents. In effect, this
is being done at the present time. A third course of

action, overlooked to some extent, is to attack the legal problems by using specific examples in marine research programs on a case by case basis to establish precedents. One might consider this because it might be much easier to solve some of the legal problems in connection with research programs where a great deal of money is not at stake. In this way controversies could be resolved at a much lower key than they might be if considered in context of exploitation of the resources. It is possible such cases could provide landmark cases for use in the future exploitation of the sea.

As an example of this, four major United States oceanographic laboratories are involved in a deep sea research program in which they propose to drill a series of holes in the Sigsbee Knolls near the center of the Gulf of Mexico. The structure of these knolls is known to be similar to others found in shallow waters which have petroleum associated with them. These knolls are located essentially in the center of the Gulf of Mexico some hundreds of miles from shore and in thousands of meters of water, in what is now considered international waters. However, if one were to draw a line between Brownsville, Texas, and the Yucatan Peninsula, you would find that these knolls lie on what might be considered the Mexican side of the fence. The questions naturally arise: Do we have to get Mexico's permission before we drill in this area? What are our liabilities if we were to strike oil there causing massive pollution? Here is a case that might be resolved through negotiation where re-

[95]

search is the reason for bringing up the problem. It is easy to imagine this would be a more difficult situation if it came up in connection with the exploration for oil. Another example is the research area that concerns the great increase in the number of submersibles that are being used for research. We are almost to the point where we need to draft conventions to determine how these are to be operated internationally; what rights they have to operate submerged beyond the territorial waters; the right to salvage; the rights of liability, international standards, rules of the road, etc. If such conventions were drafted and accepted for research purposes, the extension to vehicles involved in exploitation might be minor. Yet it might be difficult or even impossible to get nations to agree on laws that would allow submersibles to exploit covertly the resources of their own shelf. Many similar examples such as buoys, man-in-the-sea, etc., could be attacked in the same fashion.

To summarize, I have indicated that the long term interest in the ocean is important; that it is necessary to clarify a national policy for the public order of the seas; that many alternative regimes are possible; that either the United Nations' ownership or the Flag-Nation approach seems to be the most logical at this time, although it would probably take several years to bring either into force; that timing appears to be critical in this matter and, lastly, that some immediate legal problems of research programs might present opportunities to establish landmark legal cases.

# MAXWELL

*Question:* You touched rather lightly on the regimes of the fisheries on the high seas. Do you feel that we should have a new convention on that or should we try to make the present one work first?

*Dr. Maxwell:* I would like to point out that all four of these conventions came at the same time. There have been changes to the fisheries convention that have come up recently. Although I am not familiar with the details on the fisheries convention, it is my understanding that all of these problems are one and the same. They involve conflicting uses of the sea and they probably ought to be considered all at the same time. The pressing question right now is the ownership of the bottom of the sea and how one handles the mineral resources of the sea. I think this should not be done without considering the uses of the water itself at the same time, because if you do one without the other I think you are going to run into conflict.

*Question:* In the recent war, you had the problem of a three mile limit. On the other hand, is it not Peru that has a 200 mile limit?

*Dr. Maxwell:* Peru and several other South American countries.

*Question:* Where do you draw the line and what limit do you think ought to be a reasonable limit that all nations should observe?

*Mr. Abel:* It is a conflict between international and

[97]

national waters of the principals, and what is called the right of free and innocent passage, so there are many places where within this three mile limit the boundaries of two countries would cross, it would not be a right of passage. In general, for most of these international straits, the right of free and innocent passage is specifically granted. Any vessel of any country may pass through in transit, provided it was doing so for a normal commercial or similar reason.

*Dr. Maxwell:* This is a good example of some of the conflicts of uses of the sea that come up. For example, the military, the Navy in particular, is extremely concerned that one not extend the limits of territorial waters out any farther than three miles because it closes off some of these straits and makes them territorial waters. On the other hand, the fishing people are pressing hard to move the boundary out as far as possible in order to obtain sovereign rights over the fish. It is a conflict of interest. It has been only recently that we have extended our own fishing rights out to twelve miles, and this is something that we would not agree to in the 1950 and 1958 conferences. If we had agreed at that time, this solution probably would have been adopted internationally rather than being solved on a piecemeal basis as is being done at the present time.

*Question:* There are many examples on hand of conflict between countries where there is a problem of alteration of river waters. It seems to me there may

be a future possibility of so-called rivers in the sea
being altered by one country to the detriment of another country. For example, we can trace chemicals
and other matter that originated in the Amazon river
right up to the Caribbean. Do you know of any regulations that are being contemplated to cover this
problem?

*Dr. Maxwell:* I do not know of any specific regulations that are being contemplated at this time. I do
know however, that one of the problems that has
come up is the pollution of the ocean and how one
avoids it. For example, one of the resources of the sea
is actually using it as a waste basket to dump trash
into. This is a very great resource of the ocean, but we
have to put some control on this so that one man's
garbage does not ruin another man's front yard. It is
the kind of thing that has to be discussed internationally, on perhaps a specific case basis rather than as
a broad generality.

*Question:* It is true that most of the nations a long
time ago agreed to have a three mile limit. What I
am thinking about is whether you know of any activity
or the possibility of a treaty for under the seas. Do
you believe we could get our Defense Department to
make such an agreement?

*Dr. Maxwell:* First of all I would like to clarify this.
The three mile limit is not accepted by everybody in
the world. This is what the United States recognizes
as its territorial limits; it is 200 miles for Peru and
different widths for other countries. As I recall in a

very early report, the National Academy of Science's Committee on Oceanography proposed doing just what you mention, that is, to outlaw military operations below the sea. There are many problems here. First, how do you enforce this, particularly when you are unable to detect whether anything is going on there or not? Because it is so difficult to detect undersea operations, I think our military, the people in the Navy Department for example, would not like to give up the tremendous advantage they have in being able to operate in this medium. Also, I think they would argue strongly that it is not in the best interest of the United States, at this time, to get into a treaty which outlaws undersea warfare. They consider the Polaris system to be a very important potential asset to the United States and they are not prepared to give it up at this time.

*Mr. Gerard:* There is another way to deal with some of those things. It is extremely difficult to rule out things that you cannot detect, as you pointed out, but is possible to discuss special legal arrangements and perspectives for things that are declared. For example, one could conceivably make rules by agreement or by result of litigation that certain kinds of submersibles were entitled to special rights, for example, buoys marked in a certain way would have the right to be left alone, etc.

*Dr. Maxwell:* I certainly agree with that, and this is the direction in which the Intergovernmental Oceanographic Commission is proceeding at this time.

# MAXWELL

*Question:*  Could you say something about the legal aspects of the research buoys and of buoys in general?

*Dr. Maxwell:*  There are no officially accepted laws pertaining to research buoys at this time, although the Intergovernmental Oceanographic Commission is in the process of putting together some regulations on these, such as the markings of them; some of the rights and so on. This has not been accepted as international law at this time. As a matter of fact, great difficulties exist in some of the European seas in this respect. Countries such as Norway and Great Britain have put out research buoys only to have fishermen come along and pick them up. They then claim the buoys were floating loose and request salvage rights on them. This is making buoy work very uneconomical in this particular area.

*Question:*  Do you think that we have arrived at a point where there are enough kinds of regulations so that we can establish an international coast guard operated by the United Nations and take the legal problems to them?

*Dr. Maxwell:*  I do not think we have reached the point where we can agree even bilaterally between the United States and the Soviets on some of these general problems. Let me give you an example of the kind of thing you face. In the North Sea there are some regulations that say pipelines running in from offshore wells must be trenched underneath the sea floor so that they will not bother shipping. But there are certain rocky areas in the North Sea where it is difficult

[101]

and not economically feasible to bury pipelines. Since the North Sea is not a deep ocean, only on the order of forty to sixty feet deep, a problem has arisen where a Dutch company has proposed to put a pipeline from one of the offshore wells into the Netherlands. It turns out that the pipeline would be located in the sea lane where the tankers go into Rotterdam with only a foot of water under them at the present time. If you put a pipeline in this area without burying it, then the tankers could no longer get into Rotterdam. How do you get these competing interests of this magnitude to give in? These are the kinds of problems that you face over and over again.

*Question:* How about the international coast guard idea?

*Dr. Maxwell:* I do not know. We have seen the United Nations attempt to operate a peace-keeping force, but this has not been eminently successful. Whether it would be successful or not would depend, I think, primarily on whether the major maritime powers would want it or not. Certainly they have the power to do as they wish at sea. If they would agree to an international police force or coast guard, as you say, I think this would certainly make the matter work.

*Mr. Frosch:* In the area of surface motion on the sea there is a very large body of law and there is very little difficulty in enforcing this. Admiralty law is practiced and dealt with daily. There are elaborate rules for just who has rights and precedents, the rights of anchorage, etc., and most coast guards do not spend their time enforcing those laws, they spend their time usually enforcing local laws in local waters and investigating and providing the legal background, so it seems to me that the present admiralty law is a much better base to start on. There are the official treaty laws, the kind that are in effect in Antarctica, etc. In Antarctica, though, no one really cares. In these other cases we have to use precedents from admiralty law where there has been something at stake and extend it to other kinds of operations.

*Dr. Maxwell:* It is interesting to note that in admiralty law these cases, as they come up, come under the jurisdiction of one state or another, and they are taken to court in one of the existing nations. If there were an international coast guard, one might suspect that this would have to go to an international court for judgment, and it is very doubtful that this would work at the present time.

*Question:* Lately there has been quite a lot of talk about establishing new islands at various points offshore and I am just wondering what the ownership of these islands is going to be. Is there going to be a new nation?

*Dr. Maxwell:* I do not know how to answer that specifically. I know there was an example off the coast of California that I am sure Dr. Schaefer could give you some details on, but this ambiguous definition of who owns the bottom of the ocean is part of this question, and it turns out that if you were to drill a

hole, say halfway between the United States and
Hawaii, you would have to go to the Department of
the Interior of the United States to get permission,
because the Department of Interior says that this is
part of the United States. How far out they want to
claim is up to their own interpretation.

*Dr. Frosch*: The rights and duties in respect to platforms and artificial islands are all spelled out in these
conventions in great detail. When it comes to something in the area of the high seas you are still under
the jurisdiction of your sovereign, and anything you
do out there you will be doing with its permission and
under its flag. You cannot really go out there and set
up your own kingdom. I did want to call attention to
some of these points in relation to the international
coast guard.

*Question:* How many nations or participants are
there in the intergovernmental conference? Does it
consist of all nations or is it just being led by the
United States, France, England, and Russia?

*Dr. Maxwell:* No, the membership of the Intergovernmental Oceanographic Commission is about sixty
nations in number now. Switzerland, for example, does
not have a coastline, but is a member of the oceanographic commission.

*Question:* Are these people really contributing to
this or are they just being advised what is going on?

*Dr. Maxwell:* Some of these nations are very active.

Much of the action is dominated by the United States and the Soviet Union because they have the most activity in this area, but certainly the other nations play a very active and important role.

# VIII

# FREEDOM FROM THE SEA SURFACE

William B. McLean, Ph.D.

*Technical Director, U.S. Naval Ordnance Test Station, China Lake, California*

I am going to violate the orderly progression from research to the practical. I shall discuss something that is possible but not necessarily practical, namely, the proposition of getting away from the sea surface. However, I think this makes a natural extension on the discussion of the law of the sea, because it certainly will make the law of the sea more difficult.

Travel on the sea surface, up until the last decade, has been primarily limited to the interface between the sea and the air, because of man's dependence on air as a means of propulsion. Both sails and internal combustion engines demand air for their proper operation. However, since the establishment of the nuclear engine, we really have the freedom to operate in the oceans without the use of air. One can conclude that this freedom will be a welcome relief, as I do not have to belabor the point that the ocean sometimes gets rough. In fact, even things as large in size as aircraft carriers can be broken in two by the force of the waves.

In the future, man will be able to join most of the other species of animals and be able to travel either completely above or completely below this interface which exists between the air and the water. During World War II the German submarines demonstrated that they could enter and leave harbors without the necessity of traveling on the surface. Keeping our transport ships away from the surface offers several commercial advantages, but I am not prepared to discuss whether this really makes them practical. First, protection from surface weather will allow our ships to proceed at a constant speed, and therefore arrive at their ports on a predictable schedule. Such scheduling will allow a much higher utilization of port facilities. Second, submerged transport will allow our ships to go underneath the ice and provide utilization for the entire year of ports which at present can only be used in the summer. This is very important along the northern coasts of Canada and Russia. Third, submarine transport will make possible deliveries to points along the coast which at present do not have harbor facilities. The possibility of drilling into deep cliffs, with a sufficiently large hole to allow submarines to enter, I think is a possibility in the future, although it may not be a practicality.

In case you are thinking that undersea installations are something that may occur in the far distant future, I shall show some pictures of undersea installations which exist at present. Dr. Carl Austin can help answer some questions relative to undersea installations. He has been spending the past year visiting installations which exist throughout the world.

Mining underneath the sea has been in process for something like three hundred fifty years, since King James VI of Scotland is reported to have toured such an installation which started on shore and ended up on an island out in the ocean. Some of the major installations, such as this machine shop, are of fairly impressive size below the ocean. This particular shop is ten meters square and about one hundred fifty meters long, and exists off the shore of Nova Scotia, some nine hundred meters below sea level. Large chambers have been built underground for the storage of gas. Since the entrance to this chamber is through a forty-one inch shaft, it could just as well have been built below the sea. This one was completed by Fenix and Scisson and on completion they threw a formal party where all the guests had to arrive through the forty-one inch shaft. Drilling machines to make large-diameter holes are now available. This particular hole is twenty-one feet in diameter with a smooth finish. Construction of very extensive facilities in the bedrock of the ocean is not only feasible now, but one finds that more than forty thousand people somewhere in the world are working on a daily basis in a one-atmosphere environment, with the sea over their heads.

To me, the most exciting possibility relative to international law and utilization of the ocean is the possibility of creating an experimental city which could be located completely below the ocean. Entrance to this city would be by submersibles through water-locks. Because of the incompressibility of water, such locks are much different from airlocks in that very little expenditure of energy is required to allow a fairly large vehicle to transit from a high pressure region to a low pressure region. The only energy required is to take care of the compressibility of the materials of which the vehicle is composed. Nuclear reactors can supply the energy necessary to operate such a city. Reactors of adequate size are already in existence, although, as we have heard, they are still somewhat expensive. For the use of a nuclear reactor, large quantities of cooling water are immediately available outside of any undersea city.

The problems of the production of air and the cleansing of the air from pollution have been solved on a small scale for our nuclear submarines, and I see no reason why the principles cannot be extended to the proportions needed for a city. If the experimental city can be made completely closed-cycle, so that we can use our wastes and hydroponic tanks to grow food, we will have learned some lessons that may help in this other problem that was just mentioned of how to get rid of our wastes, and perhaps we can apply these same solutions to some of the cities which exist on the surface of the earth.

The problem of water, I think, is quite easy for such an underseas city. The waste heat from the nuclear reactor which is going to be needed to provide power should produce adequate fresh water. If additional water is needed in such a city for anything like hydroponic tanks, we have available today semipermeable membranes, which if placed between the ocean and the internal cavity can separate out the salts and allow fresh water to flow into the one-atmosphere environment.

It seems that all the parts of a self-contained undersea city seem to exist with the exception of the vehicles which are needed for communication, recrea-

# FREEDOM FROM
# THE SEA SURFACE

tion and exploration outside the city. We need systems
which will provide people with mobility under the
high pressures which will exist outside of their homes.
Fortunately, there are many people and organiza-
tions now working on vehicles, which will probably
produce a wide variety of new vehicles with quite a
variety of different characteristics. At the present, we
are struck with the fact that such vehicles need high
visibility, and some of the designs which we are working on are directed towards giving all-round vision.

I think I have only a few slides of vehicles, but I can
refer you to any of the current magazine articles which
show a great variety of underseas vehicles in the
process of being developed. I believe that underseas
cities practically anywhere we want them in the ocean
can be possible, and the ability to establish complete
self-sufficiency below the sea surface may have some
very important political and economic effects. The
existence, for instance, of an undersea city would have
provided Neville Shute with a happy ending for his
novel *On the Beach.* I believe that the theme of this
conference, "Man Returns to the Sea," can be real-
ized literally and that such a return can produce for
the race the protection which it may need from the
complete extinction which Neville Shute has predicted.

QUESTIONS

*Question:* Why would we want to rush into underwater cities until it is absolutely necessary?
*Dr. McLean:* That is always the first question asked.

I think that the answer comes mostly in the area that we need to demonstrate that it is possible, so that we shall not be excluded from the future possibility by some of the legal restrictions, mentioned by Dr. Maxwell, which are in the process of being formulated.

*Question:* Is there a coordination between this project of concept of cities under the sea and the man in the sea program?

*Dr. McLean:* I think both kinds of investigation are important; man in the sea would probably be limited to depths of less than a thousand feet. If you can get a man in a one-atmosphere environment, then there is probably no limit as to the depth to which he can go. It is simply a matter of getting the proper vehicles to carry him down and back. There is no problem of decompression so long as he rides at one atmosphere from the installation on the bottom to the surface. He is perfectly comfortable and he can move about freely if he has the proper protection. That is the reason we are concentrating on vehicles with all around visibility to give him essentially the same capabilities that man on land has. One of the things that we have been very pleased with is the fact that when you are in a transparent capsule you have the feeling that you have more visibility than you do with a face mask, and you feel that if you had the tools in front of you, you could work with them perhaps even more comfortably than you can when you are diving with a mask.

*Question:* Is this a project of Naval Ordnance?

# FREEDOM FROM
# THE SEA SURFACE

*Dr. McLean:* No, this is not an established project. This is just a projection; it is a possibility and not a practicality.

*Question:* Some of us here have actually drilled to rather great depths in the ocean bottom. Mr. Bascom has experience in that area. The sedimentary structures in the ocean bottom do not seem to lend themselves to large cabins. The rock we find there is very unconsolidated and therefore these cities beneath the sea would probably be located in some of the more consolidated rock. Could you tell us about that sort of environment?

*Dr. McLean:* I would like to refer that question to Dr. Austin.

*Dr. Austin:* We look at the continental shelf areas as being about twenty percent exposed bare bedrock, based on the data that we have. On a world-wide basis, the best estimates that we can find from literature, as well as from personal experience, would be that of the overall ocean floor perhaps as much as forty percent would be accessible for this type of operation. We do not require bare rock exposure; with existing technology we can handle several hundred feet. Most people in the oil business are very familiar with the Gulf Coast, and here this is not a good idea. There is no technological problem involved, but there is a tremendous expense problem. We do feel that there are a great many areas which right at the start we are looking very hard at, as being, we think, reasonably consolidated rock, and many of these we can work.

# McLEAN

*Question:* (After a picture of a machine shop in Nova Scotia.) Is there a practical reason for that, or was that purely research, and why Nova Scotia?
*Dr. McLean:* This is a machine shop supporting the upkeep of the very extensive mining operations. They are repairing their various tools and machines rather than bringing them back to the surface.

*Question:* What are the forces that are involved on submersible craft?
*Dr. McLean:* I do not know whether I want to make it sound impossible or just difficult, but I think that modern technology is such that there are no real problems with pressure. We have mines, for instance, that are now operating at a depth of two miles and pumping the water back to the surface, and the pressures they have to work against are the same that one would have in the ocean at a depth of two miles, so that the commercial hardware to pump at the pressures we are talking about is readily available. You have to have materials that have a high strength to weight ratio.

# IX

# REMARKS AT GROUNDBREAKING CEREMONIES FOR THE MARINE BIOLOGY LABORATORY

Ralph M. Paiewonsky

*Governor of the Virgin Islands*

In behalf of the people of the Virgin Islands and its Government, I welcome you here on what very well might be noted as an historic occasion.

Here we are on a beautiful island surrounded by seas whose clear depths have been an invitation to mankind for centuries and perhaps for centuries beyond our knowledge. Yet they are the virgin seas, and their secrets are untold.

Today, many of the finest minds of the scientific world are gathered to launch a program to fathom those secrets. They seek beyond the known bounty of the sea to find the unknown which we all believe to exist there. Sources of life and sustenance—sources of hope for the survival of future generations and for the maintenance of a strong and peaceful society.

We of the Virgin Islands, are honored that the waters which gently form our shores have been selected by Fairleigh Dickinson University as the most appropriate for studies to carry out the theme of "Man Returning to the Sea for Knowledge and Abundance."

We welcome the interest of the world of science in this program and assure you of our continuing welcome and assistance as you develop the facilities planned for this unique and promising marine biology laboratory.

I am excited, as you are, about the possibilities of this project. I must confess that my own background is not entirely in government. Many years were spent in business here, and in 1932 I was engaged in research in sea water fermentation from which a rum distillation process was developed and, as a result, the rum production of the Virgin Islands became one of our major industries.

My interest in the sea, therefore, is more than academic.

It is not for that reason, however, that I wish to make this greeting something more than the usual, formal, administrative handshake. There are many elements present in this occasion which touch me personally and which have significance to all Virgin Islanders.

I think that I should first address my thought to Dr. Peter Sammartino, President of Fairleigh Dickinson University, whose knowledge, inspiration, and conviction have combined to bring us here today.

It can be said of Dr. Sammartino, as it can be said of relatively few, that he is a man of vision. In our conversations he has impressed me as one with the rare combination of academic insight, idealistic aims, and practical understanding necessary to conceive and carry out a project dedicated to the long-reaching needs of mankind. There are others concerned with the implications of oceanology. I doubt if there are many who have approached the subject with the breadth and depth of vision that Dr. Sammartino has so enthusiastically communicated to me.

The theme that he suggested for this project, and I repeat, "Man Returning to the Sea for Knowledge and Abundance", carries us far beyond the relatively modest beginning that we make here today. It is a broad stroke of the brush, not a pencilled scribble, and it contains the assurance of long effort to achieve the implied promise.

Dr. Sammartino has said that study of the resources of the sea—exploration of its wealth of elements necessary to the continued physical and economic welfare of mankind on earth—is more essentially important than conquest of space.

Although the urgencies of time and competition and, perhaps, the more mind-reeling concepts of space exploration have led us in that direction, there are many who agree that the sea offers more immediate and useful rewards. I will leave that to my scientifically informed and dedicated guests.

Next, I should turn my thought to the name of the founder of Fairleigh Dickinson University, and his son whose generous donation of ten acres of valuable St. Croix real estate has helped to make this possible.

We of the Virgin Islands, are proud of that association, a long association during which the Fairleigh Dickinson family has contributed more than material things. Aside from my personal and treasured enjoyment of their friendship, we of the islands, have benefitted in many ways from their high sense of civic and community responsibility and their participation in our constant efforts to improve our health and educational facilities.

I think you know how hard we have worked on these islands to make them truly a showplace of democracy, and we are particularly proud of our accomplishments in the field of education. In addition to our progress in elementary and secondary schools, we have created a pearl in our academic diadem, the College of the Virgin Islands. Although presently offering a two-year course in most subjects, we are planning to extend the curriculum in the near future to provide a full four-year degree program.

The presence of a branch of Fairleigh Dickinson University here furthers our hopes for the recognition of this area as a scientific and educational center as well, as it has become so favorably known as a heaven for tourists and a haven for business and industry.

In fact, the remarkable growth of Fairleigh Dickinson University itself is an inspiration to us who are working diligently to build our own educational institutions as rapidly and soundly as possible. It is hard to believe that in less than twenty-five years Fairleigh Dickinson has become the eighth largest privately supported institution of higher learning in the United States. It started as a private residence and now has five campuses in the northern part of the state of New Jersey, with an enrollment of twenty thousand day and evening students in four undergraduate colleges, a school of dentistry, and a graduate school. In addition, it owns campuses in France and England and has summer programs in Mexico and Italy.

And now, we welcome it to St. Croix.

Such progress in twenty-five years is hard to believe. But that is the type of progress that we in the Virgin Islands do believe; it is the pace that we have set for ourselves.

Earlier I referred to this as an historic occasion. I believe it is, and I have that strange sense we sometimes have when we are subconsciously aware of the importance of an event.

If we had the gift of seeing into the future as well as we can reconstruct and imagine the past, what would we see?

Looking into the past, we can imagine the primitive ships of Christopher Columbus as they hopefully sailed toward these beaches in search of fresh water—in 1493. Today we view the same beaches as hopefully, but seeking something far more complex and more promising.

I like to think that we who are met here today stand on a new frontier. As Dr. Sammartino has remarked, "The seas are the last frontiers of all nations." If we are the advance scouts, surveying the territory to be explored, I know that legions of scientists and students will follow to carry out that exploration—to extract the bounty of the sea for the good of all mankind.

As people who live surrounded by these beneficent waters, we pray that they will yield their wealth and the wisdom of their deeps to those who are here dedicated to that search.

[118]

## X

# STATEMENT ON THE ESTABLISHMENT OF A MARINE BIOLOGY LABORATORY

Peter Sammartino, Ph.D.

*Chancellor, Fairleigh Dickinson University*

The sea is man's last frontier on the earth. At the present time we are utilizing very little of it to meet the needs of food and minerals for the human race. Furthermore, we must learn how to conserve its purity and to prevent senseless exploitation. Fairleigh Dickinson University proposes to harness and to integrate the resources of the institution in order to meet this challenge to mankind.

Our newly-established laboratories at St. Croix, Virgin Islands, are admirably suited as a center for operations which will:

1. Allow our students to enrich their courses of study in marine biology and engineering by providing stays of various duration at our laboratory;
2. Provide a base for research in the various aspects of oceanology;
3. Provide a training center for teachers of science so that they in turn can pass on to their students an understanding of the importance of the sea.

We have been used to thinking about the sea around us as a dumping ground for our refuse, and not as an

[119]

# ESTABLISHMENT OF A
# MARINE BIOLOGY LABORATORY

integral part of our planet earth. We have had recently an unfortunate example of how oil cast off from a ship created a national disaster in England. We find that deep sea fish hundreds of miles offshore have a higher incidence of pesticides than the legal tolerance would approve. The oceans are not as vast as they once seemed. And even now, the resources that may seem endless to us may diminish before our very eyes. Schools of millions of small fish can be exhausted in the sea, just as in the United States one state after another lost its primacy in lumbering until finally we learned the lesson of conservation.

Yes, this is man's last frontier. But we must learn to use it wisely before it is too late. Even then it is probably too late to use it effectively to prevent the world famine that is predicted for 1975 by William Paddock, former president of the National Academy of Sciences. Research, no matter how assiduously pursued, proceeds slowly and after the basic research, the implementation takes an even greater toll of years. In the meantime, the fantastic rate of growth of population nullifies our feeble efforts to utilize the resources of the sea. And to add to the problem, people, unless they get to the critical starving stage, do not take easily to new types of food. As Dr. Paddock says, "Have you seen anyone eating algae lately?"— or I might add, bread made from fish flour?

If the human race were wiser, we would stop the crazy race for the moon and concentrate on the intelligent use of the sea. But the human race is not wise and so we expend our greatest energy on space, and slower pace to the sea, and probably somewhere in the seventies millions of people will suddenly die from starvation and then, and only then, will we awaken to the realization that the sea will help us to prevent future self-annihilation of the human race.

It is almost with a sense of impending holocaust that faces the world, that I dedicate the marine biology laboratory of Fairleigh Dickinson University as a step toward the future, for no university worthy of its name can afford not to concern itself with man's last effort for survival.